Test
Your
English
Idioms

Peter Watcyn-Jones

Illustrated by Ross Thomson

PENGUIN ENGLISH

PENGUIN BOOKS
Published by the Penguin Group
Penguin Books Ltd, 27 Wrights Lane, London W8 5TZ, England
Penguin Books USA Inc., 375 Hudson Street, New York, New York 10014, USA
Penguin Books Australia Ltd, Ringwood, Victoria, Australia
Penguin Books Canada Ltd, 10 Alcorn Avenue, Toronto, Ontario, Canada M4V 3B2
Penguin Books (NZ) Ltd, 182–190 Wairau Road, Auckland 10, New Zealand

Penguin Books Ltd, Registered Offices: Harmondsworth, Middlesex, England

First published 1990
10 9 8 7 6 5 4 3

Copyright © Peter Watcyn-Jones, 1990
All rights reserved

Filmset in Century Schoolbook

Made and printed in Great Britain by
BPCC Hazell Books
Aylesbury, Bucks, England
Member of BPCC Ltd

CONTENTS

INTRODUCTION

TEST YOUR ENGLISH IDIOMS is a welcome addition to the *Test Your Vocabulary* series and is intended for intermediate/advanced students. Altogether, the book contains more than 750 idioms in current use and, as the title suggests, the emphasis is on testing rather than teaching. Subsequently, the book can be a useful complement to a wide variety of reference books and dictionaries on idioms.

In keeping with the *Test Your Vocabulary* series, there is a wide variety of tests, ranging from multiple-choice exercises, crosswords, exercises where you have to match up an idiom with a suitable definition, completing sentences, rewriting sentences, to picture tests, where you have to choose an appropriate caption for each drawing. In addition, there are tests on idioms of comparison ("as brown as a berry"), proverbs and idioms to do with colours, parts of the body, animals, and so on.

TEST YOUR ENGLISH IDIOMS can be used in class with a teacher or for self-study. To facilitate the latter, a key is included which not only gives the correct answers but also gives detailed explanations when necessary. Students using this book should find the learning of idioms both stimulating and enjoyable and, hopefully, start to develop a real sensitivity to the language.

In choosing the idioms for this book I have naturally consulted a number of dictionaries and reference books. The following can be warmly recommended:

Longman Dictionary of English Idioms (Longman)
Dictionary of English Idioms   Michael J. Wallace (Collins)
Working with English Idioms   David Peaty (Nelson)
English Idioms and How to Use Them   Jennifer Seidl & W. McMordie (Oxford University Press)
A Learner's Dictionary of English Idioms   Isabel McCaig & Martin H. Manser (Oxford University Press)
Oxford Dictionary of Current Idiomatic English, Volume 2: Phrase, Clause & Sentence Idioms A.P. Cowie, R. Mackin & I.R. McCaig (Oxford University Press)

TO THE STUDENT

This book will help you to learn a lot of new English words. But in order for the new words to become "fixed" in your mind, you need to test yourself again and again. Here is one method you can use to help you learn the words.

1. Read through the instructions carefully for the test you are going to try. Then try the test, writing your answers **in pencil**.
2. When you have finished, check your answers and correct any mistakes you have made. Read through the test again, paying special attention to the words you didn't know or got wrong.
3. Try the test again five minutes later. You can do this either by covering up the words (for example, in the picture tests) or by asking a friend to test you. Repeat this until you can remember all the words.
4. **Rub out your answers.**
5. Try the test again the following day. (You should remember most of the words.)
6. Finally, plan to try the test at least twice again within the following month. After this most of the words will be "fixed" in your mind.

1 Definitions 1

Match up the definitions on the left (1–16) with the correct idiom on the right (a–p).

1	clever, intelligent *e*	**a**	all thumbs
2	inquisitive, curious *k*	**b**	bedridden
3	rich, wealthy *o*	**c**	bigheaded
4	cruel *h*	**d**	black and blue all over
5	stupid, unintelligent *n*	**e**	brainy
6	young, inexperienced *p*	**f**	cheeky
7	old (of a person) *j*	**g**	hair-raising
8	very clumsy, awkward *a*	**h**	heartless
9	impudent *f*	**i**	keyed up
10	stubborn *m*	**j**	long in the tooth
11	too weak to leave one's bed *b*	**k**	nosy
12	terrifying *g*	**l**	off colour
13	conceited, vain, boastful *c*	**m**	pigheaded
14	tense, excited *i*	**n**	thick
15	ill, not well *l*	**o**	well off
16	covered with bruises *d*	**p**	wet behind the ears

2 Choose the idiom 1

Choose the word or phrase which best completes each sentence.

1 I really must go and lie down for a while; I've got a .... headache.

   a cutting   **b** splitting   **c** ringing   **d** cracking

2 Stop .... about the bush, James! Just tell me exactly what the problem is.

   a rushing   **b** hiding   **c** beating   **d** moving

3 I usually buy my clothes .... It's cheaper than going to a dressmaker.

   a off the peg   **b** on the house   **c** in public   **d** on the shelf

4 David's leaving on Friday. I suggest we all .... and get him a going-away present. £1 each should do.

   a dish out   **b** chip in   **c** pass the buck   **d** pay on the nail

5 The sky got very dark and soon it began to .... down.

   a roar   **b** bath   **c** bucket   **d** pouring

6 My father .... when he found out that I'd damaged the car.

   a hit the roof   **b** saw pink elephants   **c** made my blood boil
   d brought the house down

7 If you want a flat in the centre of the city you have to pay through the .... for it.

   a teeth   **b** back of your head   **c** nose   **d** arm

8 I caught the last bus by the skin of my ....

   a mouth   **b** leg   **c** neck   **d** teeth

9 Because the owner wanted a quick sale, the house went for .... – only £30,000.

   a loose change   **b** a song   **c** a loaf of bread   **d** a smile

10 You didn't think I was being serious, did you, Brian! It was a joke! I was pulling your ...., that's all!

   a thumb   **b** hair   **c** toe   **d** leg

11 The accident was caused by a taxi driver .... the traffic lights.

   a rushing   **b** missing   **c** jumping   **d** beating

12 Lend me £20, please, John. I'm .... at the moment.

    a broke   **b** down the drain   **c** stuck up   **d** a bit thick

13 She would do anything for her youngest son. He was the .... of her eye.

    a plum   **b** centre   **c** star   **d** apple

14 I always get .... in my stomach before visiting the dentist.

    a worms   **b** butterflies   **c** crabs   **d** hedgehogs

15 Those second-hand Walkmans are selling like .... If you want one, you'd better buy one now before they're all gone.

    a shooting stars   **b** fresh bread   **c** hot cakes   **d** wild oats

3 Idioms with "at"

Fill in the missing words in the sentences below. Choose from the following:

at a loose end	at death's door	at one's wits' end*
at a loss	at fault	at random
at a pinch	at first sight	at short notice
at a standstill	at least	at sixes and sevens
at all costs	at loggerheads	at the crack of dawn
at all hours	at most	at will
at best	at once	

(* change as appropriate)

1   We must .... catch the 7.30 train. Otherwise we won't get to the meeting in time.

2   It is difficult to know who's .... in the matter. Perhaps we're all to blame.

3   It's late. I think you'd better go to bed now, darling. Remember, you've got to get up .... tomorrow.

4   Since it's his first offence he'll probably get off with a warning – .... a small fine.

5   If you're .... this weekend, Joan, why not come over for a meal? It'll give us a chance to catch up on some gossip.

6   I may be getting on a bit, but I'm certainly not .... yet! I hope to live for at least another ten to fifteen years!

7   When her daughter didn't come home on the last bus with the other girls, Mrs Jenkins was .... – she was terrified that something dreadful had happened to her.

8   Like you, I'm .... to explain the sudden fall in share prices. I've absolutely no idea what can have caused it.

9   When Richard Burton saw Elizabeth Taylor it was a classic case of love ....

10 Traffic was .... this morning because of an accident on the A21.

11 I'm afraid everything's .... this week. Both the secretaries are ill and no one knows where anything is.

12 The hotel wasn't that modern, but .... it was cheap and reasonably clean.

13 I've got room in the car for three – four ....

14 Mrs Smith's daughter is terrible, isn't she? Out .... and never a kind word to anyone.

15 You should be able to sell your stereo equipment for £200 – .... £250.

16 If you don't get out .... then I shall have you thrown out.

17 Pamela and David are always .... I really can't imagine why they got married in the first place. They've got absolutely nothing in common.

18 A chameleon is a remarkable creature – it is able to change the colour of its skin ....

19 You can't expect me to work overtime .... such ....! I need to be told at least two days in advance.

20 I was in a hurry for my train, so I chose a book ....

What are they saying? 1

Look at the drawings below and try to work out what the people are saying. Mark the appropriate letter (a–l) in each of the speech bubbles. Choose from the following:

a "I've got a splitting headache again, Arthur."

b "Well, it looks as though the rain has set in for the night."

c "Isn't there any other way for you to make a living?"

d "I must have caught a cold on the way."

e "He's a bit absent-minded sometimes."

f "Not too loud! She's all ears, you know."

g "Jack's always had green fingers."

h "Everyone has an off-day now and then!"

i "Give me a hand, would you?"

j "You're down in the dumps again, aren't you, Albert? I can tell, you know."

k "He's full of beans, isn't he?"

l "You lost your tongue or something? For the last time – where to?"

Complete the crossword 1

Complete the following crossword.

ACROSS

1   You'd better keep away from Mr Hollis. He's got a .... to pick with you.

2   I won't be long; I'm just .... to the loo.

6   Can I give you a ring next week, John? I can't talk now, I'm afraid. I'm a bit .... for time.

9   Charles will never get married. He's a confirmed ....

10 What does this say? I can't make head nor .... of it.

13 Oh, what *is* the word? I know it! It's on the tip of my ....

14 Her husband's snoring began to get on her ....

15 We were in a hurry, so I tried to .... the waiter's eye in order to pay the bill.

18 Poor dog! It can't be getting enough to eat. Look at it! It's all .... and bones!

19 According to my family .... my great-great-grandfather came from Finland.

DOWN

1 It was no accident. He killed her in cold ....

3 I hate going to bed early. I've always been a bit of a .... owl.

4 Speak up! I'm a bit hard of ....

5 To most people, a Rolls-Royce is still something of a .... symbol.

7 Jenny's very irritable today. She's like a .... with a sore head.

8 She passed the exam with .... colours.

11 The pupils found it hard to keep a .... face when their teacher slipped on a banana skin.

12 I'll have a beer. No, on .... thoughts, make that a shandy.

16 All right! All right! Keep your .... on! There's no need to lose your temper.

17 You shouldn't .... fun of the way he speaks English. He's only been learning it for two years.

6 Complete the sentences 1

Complete sentences 1–15 by choosing an ending from a–o.

1 She was feeling down in the mouth because ...
2 He was hard up this month because he ...
3 We decided to get a move on because we ...
4 After spending the whole day walking around the shops in London, we ...
5 She was late for work this morning because she ...
6 The secretary asked me to hold the line while she ...
7 It was a secret, so I ...
8 Now that he's out of work he ...
9 He can't read a note of music – he ...
10 I was feeling a bit under the weather so I ...
11 As we had over two hours to wait for our train, we ...
12 I can't say I recognise her but ...
13 The room was so quiet that you ...
14 Don't expect Paul to remember anything. He's ...
15 If you play your cards right you ...

a ... promised to keep it under my hat.
b ... her name rings a bell.
c ... got a memory like a sieve.
d ... decided not to go to work.
e ... plays everything by ear.
f ... she and her boyfriend had just broken up.
g ... didn't want to miss the last bus.
h ... could end up being manager by the time you're thirty.
i ... could hear a pin drop.
j ... had a lot of bills to pay.
k ... finds it hard to make ends meet.
l ... got caught in a traffic-jam.
m ... decided to kill time by going into a pub for a drink.
n ... were dead beat.
o ... put me through to the manager.

Write your answers here:

1	2	3	4	5	6	7	8	9	10	11	12	13	14	15

7 Idioms of comparison 1

Choose the word or phrase which best completes each sentence.

1 Where is everyone? It's as silent as .... in here!

   a Sunday   **b** the grave   **c** death   **d** a tomb

2 Jimmy's feeling a bit under the weather today, but I expect he'll be as right as .... by the weekend.

   a an athlete   **b** sunshine   **c** rain   **d** roses

3 I'll never eat and drink as much as that again! I was as sick as a .... on the way home!

   a dog   **b** horse   **c** pig   **d** poodle

4 Ask David to give you a hand moving the furniture. He's as strong as ....

   a an elephant   **b** a mountain   **c** a gorilla   **d** a horse

5 You're not getting enough to eat, Karen! Look at you! You're as thin as a ....

   a stick insect   **b** rake   **c** finger   **d** wire

6 We can't eat this meat – it's as tough as ....!

   a canvas   **b** old boots   **c** rubber   **d** stale bread

7 You shouldn't have frightened her like that. Poor thing! She went as white as ....!

   a a sheet   **b** snow   **c** milk   **d** whitewash

8 Nothing ever seems to bother Colin. No matter what happens, he always seems to remain as cool as ....

   a cold feet   **b** ice-cream   **c** a cucumber   **d** an Eskimo

9 You'll have to shout, I'm afraid. My father's as deaf as ....

   a a leaf   **b** a post   **c** a politician   **d** a stone

10 It's hard to believe Brian and Stephen are brothers, isn't it? They're as different as ....

   a Mars from Jupiter   **b** milk from honey   **c** chalk from cheese
   d margarine from butter

11 Although we had been told that the film was very exciting, both my wife and I found it to be as dull as ....

   a ditchwater   **b** a don   **c** a dungeon   **d** a museum

12 Honestly, Pam, ever since I've given up smoking I feel as fit as ....!

    a a fighter   **b** a fiddle   **c** a frog   **d** an athlete

13 Our dog looks very ferocious, but don't worry, Liz, Fido's as gentle as .... – especially with children.

    a a pony   **b** snowflakes   **c** a lamb   **d** washing-up liquid

14 "I hope the children didn't play you up, Doreen?"
"No, not at all, Mrs Gardener. They've been as good as ...."

    a religion   **b** gold   **c** God   **d** brass

15 "The suitcase isn't too heavy, is it?"
"No, it's as light as ...."

    a dust   **b** lightning   **c** a feather   **d** a fish

16 I wish the new secretary would cheer up! She's been as miserable as .... for the past week!

    a a monk   **b** death   **c** a banker   **d** sin

17 "By the way, have you heard the one about the Welshman, the Irishman and the pig?"
"Yes, we have. That joke's as old as ...."

    a Solomon   **b** the hills   **c** a dinosaur   **d** Jupiter

18 Of course he loves you! It's as plain as ....

    a a pancake   **b** the knob on your door   **c** the nose on your face
    d a bell

19 Kathy was as pleased as .... when she heard she had passed the exam.

    a punch   **b** a poppy   **c** a sunflower   **d** pound notes

20 I hope the computer course starts this term. We're all as keen as .... to get going.

    a coffee   **b** mustard   **c** a gigolo   **d** cornflakes

8 Choose the verb

Fill in the missing verbs. Choose from the following, using each verb once only:

bear	change	fall	lose	set
beg	do	foot	pay	tell
break	draw	hold	play	throw
call	drive	keep	put	use
catch	drop	lay	resist	waste
chair	earn	lead	run	work

1   to .... a hard bargain
2   to .... one's breath
3   to .... a business
4   to .... someone to death
5   to .... force
6   to .... a grudge
7   to .... a habit
8   to .... a living
9   to .... heart
10 to .... a hint
11 to .... a lie
12 to .... a busy life
13 to .... in love
14 to .... one's mind
15 to .... a miracle
16 to .... someone names
17 to .... a meeting
18 to .... someone's pardon
19 to .... a party
20 to .... the bill
21 to .... time in prison
22 to .... a secret
23 to .... sight of someone
24 to .... the line at something
25 to .... fire to something
26 to .... the table
27 to .... temptation
28 to .... time
29 to .... truant
30 to .... a visit

Newspaper headlines 1

Fill in the missing words in the following newspaper headlines. Choose from the following. (The words in brackets under each headline should help you.)

A FLASH IN THE PAN	FROSTY	MAKE A COMEBACK
ALL THE RAGE	GET THE CHOP	MAKE A FLYING VISIT
BLACKOUT	GETS COLD FEET	NECK AND NECK
CAUGHT IN THE ACT	GETS OUT OF HAND	ON THE DOLE
COME INTO FORCE	HIGH AND LOW	WORK TO RULE
FOR THE HIGH JUMP		

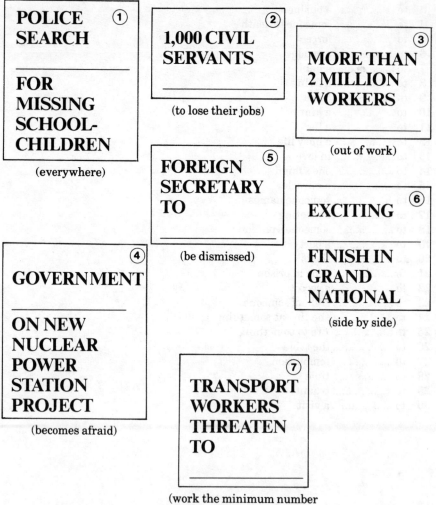

① POLICE SEARCH _____ FOR MISSING SCHOOL-CHILDREN
(everywhere)

② 1,000 CIVIL SERVANTS _____
(to lose their jobs)

③ MORE THAN 2 MILLION WORKERS _____
(out of work)

⑤ FOREIGN SECRETARY TO _____
(be dismissed)

④ GOVERNMENT _____ ON NEW NUCLEAR POWER STATION PROJECT
(becomes afraid)

⑥ EXCITING _____ FINISH IN GRAND NATIONAL
(side by side)

⑦ TRANSPORT WORKERS THREATEN TO _____
(work the minimum number of hours – no overtime)

2-HOUR ⑧
_____

CAUSES LUNCHTIME CHAOS

(electricity failure)

NEW VIDEO PHONES JUST ⑨
_____

(a passing novelty)

AMERICAN PRESIDENT TO ⑩
_____

TO THE MIDDLE EAST

(make a quick trip)

_____
WELCOME FOR PRIME MINISTER ⑪

(unfriendly)

PEACEFUL DEMONSTRA-TION ⑫
_____

(gets out of control)

LEATHER EARRINGS ⑬
_____

(very fashionable)

RUSSIAN SPY ⑭
_____

(found spying)

FAMOUS POP STAR OF THE 70s TO ⑮
_____

(try to be popular again)

NEW IMMIGRATION LAWS ⑯
_____
ON JULY 1ST

(become law)

10 True or false? 1

Say whether the idioms in the following sentences are used correctly (true) or incorrectly (false).

		TRUE	FALSE
1	If someone is *green*, he or she is not very experienced.	[ ]	[ ]
2	If you want to get *browned off*, you have to lie in the sun all day.	[ ]	[ ]
3	I'll only buy the dog if it's *house-trained*.	[ ]	[ ]
4	If you are feeling *peckish*, you feel like something to eat.	[ ]	[ ]
5	He was a very good pianist. He was so *light-fingered*.	[ ]	[ ]
6	You would probably be very flattered if someone called you *stuck up*.	[ ]	[ ]
7	I couldn't go to work this morning. I was *laid up*.	[ ]	[ ]
8	I'm sure someone is talking about me – I can *feel my ears burning*.	[ ]	[ ]
9	To *bear fruit* means to have a lot of children.	[ ]	[ ]
10	My cousin *kicked the bucket* last week. He leaves a widow and three young children.	[ ]	[ ]
11	I've stopped going to my German classes. I've *dropped off*.	[ ]	[ ]
12	He is very rich. He has ten servants and lives with his wife and two children in *an ivory tower*.	[ ]	[ ]
13	He's not being serious. He's speaking *with his tongue in his cheek*.	[ ]	[ ]
14	Cowards don't usually *stick their necks out*.	[ ]	[ ]
15	If you can't afford the train fare or the bus fare, you can always try to *thumb a lift*.	[ ]	[ ]
16	You would probably be very pleased if someone *took you for a ride*.	[ ]	[ ]

Definitions 2

Match up the definitions on the left (1–16) with the correct idiom on the right (a–p).

1	the death penalty	**a**	a bighead
2	a drink (alcoholic) taken before one goes to bed	**b**	a black spot
3	a short sleep in a chair (not in a bed)	**c**	a blackleg
4	a success that only lasts a short time	**d**	a brainwave
5	someone who is blamed for other people's mistakes	**e**	capital punishment
6	someone who is very conceited	**f**	a catnap
7	someone who attends a party without being invited	**g**	a godsend
8	a difficulty – often hidden or unexpected	**h**	a downpour
9	a heavy shower of rain	**i**	an eyesore
10	someone who offers to work when the regular workers are on strike	**j**	a flash in the pan
11	unnecessary bureaucracy	**k**	a gatecrasher
12	a sudden, clever thought or idea	**l**	a nightcap
13	something which is unexpected but which is very much needed and appreciated	**m**	red tape
14	a search for something which has no hope of being successful	**n**	a scapegoat
15	something very unpleasant to look at (e.g. a building)	**o**	a snag
16	a place in a road where accidents often happen	**p**	a wild goose chase

12 Choose the idiom 2

Choose the word or phrase which best completes each sentence.

1 I haven't had an accident yet but I've had a number of .... shaves.

   a narrow   **b** near   **c** close   **d** tiny

2 My father refused to eat meat that had been fried. He had .... in his bonnet about it causing cancer.

   a a bug   **b** a bee   **c** a bull   **d** an ant

3 You really dropped .... the other day when you told Brian you'd seen his wife at the cinema. He thought she was at her mother's.

   a a brick   **b** a stone   **c** a log   **d** a plank

4 I can't stand Mr Bryant. He's always blowing his own .... – telling everyone how good he is at everything.

   a balloon   **b** breath   **c** mind   **d** trumpet

5 The escaped prisoner fought .... before he was finally overpowered.

   a head over heels   **b** tooth and nail   **c** heart and soul
   d foot and mouth

6 I didn't suspect anything at first, but when I noticed her going through the office drawers I began to smell ....

   a a rat   **b** a pig   **c** a thief   **d** a culprit

7 Jane looked .... at the shop assistant who had been rude to her.

   a arrows   **b** needles   **c** poison   **d** daggers

8 Peter was born and brought up in Hastings and knows it like the ....

   a nose on his face   **b** tip of his tongue   **c** back of his hand
   d hair on his head

9 I bought a computer last year, but I've had nothing but trouble with it. As far as I'm concerned it was £800 down the ....

   a loo   **b** sink   **c** drain   **d** plughole

10 John will never buy you a drink – he's far too ....

   a tight-fisted   **b** pigheaded   **c** highly-strung   **d** easy-going

11 I've heard that argument before and quite frankly it just doesn't ....!

   a face the music   **b** hit the nail on the head   **c** carry weight
   d hold water

12 I was already fed up with the job, but when the boss walked into my office and told me he expected me to work overtime that was the .... I quit.

    a final curtain   **b** last straw   **c** end of the line   **d** last waltz

13 He has a quick temper and easily .... off the handle.

    a leaps   **b** goes   **c** runs   **d** flies

14 I don't like turning down work, but I'll have to, I'm afraid. I've got far too much .... at the moment.

    a up my sleeve   **b** on my plate   **c** on my mind   **d** in effect

15 And that ...., Brian, is why I can't marry you!

    a in a flash   **b** on the dot   **c** off the cuff   **d** in a nutshell

13 Idioms with "in"

Fill in the missing words in the sentences below. Choose from the following:

in a rut	in season	in the nick of time
in cash	in short	in the red
in charge of	in stock	in theory
in common	in succession	in tune
in due course	in the dark	in turns
in favour of	in the limelight	in vain
in one ear and out the other	in the long run	

1 I can't think why they ever got married. They have absolutely nothing ....

2 The inexperienced teacher tried .... to control the unruly class. In the end she had to call for the headmaster.

3 "Two tins of baked beans, please."
"I'm afraid we haven't got any .... at the moment. But we should be getting some more on Thursday."

4 Last year was the third year .... that they had come top of the football league.

5 The staff took it .... to make afternoon coffee.

6 No one's been told what's going to happen at the conference yet. We're all being kept .... for some reason.

7 We got to the station .... A second later and we'd have missed our connection.

8 It must be difficult being famous. Just imagine being .... all the time; never being able to go out without being recognised.

9 This is Mrs Brightwell. She's .... marketing.

10 Although I've been trying hard to pay back my bank loan, I'm still .... In fact, I've got to go and see my bank manager about it tomorrow.

11 Strawberries cost a lot at the moment because they're not ....

12 Thank you for attending the interview, Mr Blake. You'll be hearing from us .... – probably at the end of next week.

13 Although I like teaching I sometimes feel that I'm .... I seem to be doing the same thing all the time – the job is no longer challenging enough.

14 Are you sure your piano's ....? It sounds terrible to me.

15 My Frank is tall, dark, handsome, has a marvellous job and is incredibly rich. .... he's the perfect husband!

16 Hands up all those .... capital punishment. Thank you. Now hands up all those against.

17 It costs £150 if you pay by credit card or £120 if you pay ....

18 The law may be unpopular now, but I'm sure people will soon see how good it is for the country and themselves ....

19 It's no use talking to Jane. She never listens. It's a case of ....

20 His ideas sounded wonderful ...., but they never seemed to work out in practice.

14 Have you heard the one about . . . ?

Complete the following jokes with a suitable idiom chosen from the box.
(Make any changes that may be necessary.)

a vicious circle	laugh (one's) head off
bring the house down	pull (oneself) together
down in the mouth	pull a few strings
fall head over heels in love	put (an animal) to sleep
get a word in edgeways	sleep like a log
give (someone) a good hiding	stand in (someone's) way
give (someone) a ring	strike while the iron is hot
have a leg to stand on	tell (someone) off
in (someone's) shoes	the short list

1   I once knew two acrobats who ....

2   When Albert auditioned for the part of one of the seven dwarfs in the West
    End musical "Snow White and the Seven Dwarfs", the director told him he
    had been put on ....

3   "I just don't know what to do. What would you do if you were ....?"
    "Polish them."

4   When my friend's dog was faced with four trees he didn't ....

5   "What goes 'ha, ha, hee, hee, blonk'?"
    "Someone ....!"

6   The next act is a famous puppeteer who broke into show business by
    ....

7   We close the show tonight, ladies and gentlemen, with Samson the strongest
    man in the world – who is sure to ....

8   "Doctor! Doctor! I keep thinking I'm a pair of curtains."
    "Well, ...!"

9   *Customer*: Waiter! This boiled egg is bad!
    Waiter: (looking at the egg) So it is. Shall I pick it up and .... and
                 tell it not to be bad again?

10 *Small boy*: Please miss, would you be angry and .... for something
                  I didn't do?
    Teacher: No, of course not.
    Small boy: Oh good! Then I can tell you that I haven't done my homework.

11 *Mother*:   Why have you dragged your bed out into the woodshed?
    Samantha: Because I want to ....

12 One woman I know hasn't spoken to her husband for ten years – she can't
    ....

13 *Man*: Where's your dog?
   Friend: I had to ....
   Man: Was it mad?
   Friend: Well, it wasn't exactly pleased.

14 Yesterday, five hundred men walked out of a steel mill while it was still in operation. A Union spokesman said they had to ....

15 "Doctor! Doctor! I feel like a bell."
   "Well, take these and if they don't work, ..."

16 "Why is a dentist always unhappy?"
   "Because he looks ...."

17 *Tom*: When I grow up I'm going to drive a tank.
   Dad: Well, I certainly won't ....

18 "What's round and bad-tempered?"
   " .... "

15 Rewrite the sentences 1

For each of the sentences below write a new sentence with a similar meaning. Substitute the words in italics with the word in CAPITAL LETTERS plus one of the verbs in the box. (You may need to use some of them more than once.)

get	go	keep	make	put	take

Example: I don't know which dress to buy. I can't *decide*.
MIND
I don't know which dress to buy. I can't *make up my mind*.

1 She was so beautiful that I couldn't *stop looking at* her.
EYES
....

2 Winning that prize has *made him very conceited*.
HEAD
....

3 When he was a child he loved *dismantling things* – to see how they worked.
PIECES
....

4 I do wish you'd stop biting your nails, Brian! It really *annoys me*.
NERVES
....

5 English people in general don't like *complaining* in public.
FUSS
....

6 Could you *guard* my handbag for me while I go to the toilet?
EYE
....

7 She's not really upset; she's only *pretending*.
ACT
....

8 We're moving to Bristol next week but we promise to *stay in contact with you*.
TOUCH
....

9 You *made an embarrassing mistake* when you asked him where his wife was. Didn't you realise she was dead?
FOOT
....

10 I hate the winter – it really *depresses me*.
DOWN
....

11 It was hard *not to start laughing* when she started to sing.
FACE

....

12 Many husbands often *don't appreciate their wives*; and vice-versa.
GRANTED

....

13 I happen to know the manager of the firm you've applied to for a job. I can *recommend you*, if you like.
WORD

....

14 "All this *happened* a long, long time ago," said the history teacher to the class.
PLACE

....

15 Many people nowadays find it increasingly difficult to *exist on the money they earn*.
ENDS

....

Complete the following crossword.

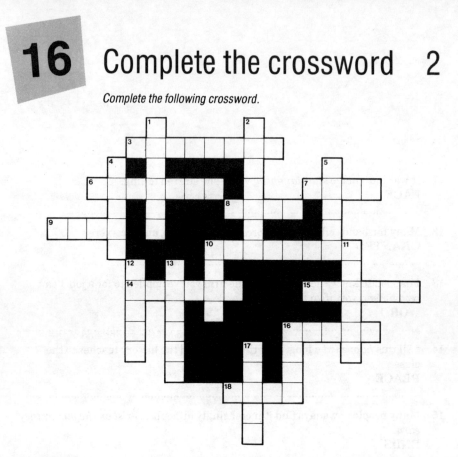

ACROSS

3   I honestly don't know what the fuss is all about! Really, Dorothy, I think you're making a .... out of a molehill.

6   People choose .... tours because they are cheap and convenient compared to planning and arranging a holiday themselves.

7   Although he was retired, he still liked to teach the odd evening class just to .... his hand in.

8   "How far is it to Littlehampton?"
    "About ten miles as the .... flies."

9   And now ladies and gentlemen, please give a big .... for tonight's stars – Ruby Taylor and the Roxettes.

10 It's nothing to do with you, so mind your own ....!

14 Sorry! I didn't mean that! It was a slip of the ...., that's all.

15 The father got a bit hot under the .... trying to explain the facts of life to his teenage son.

16 "Was it really six years ago that we last met?"
    "Yes, it was."
    "Well, I never! Time certainly ...., doesn't it?"

18 I only asked you a question. There's no need to .... my head off!

DOWN

1   As we were walking home we got caught in a thunderstorm and were
.... to the skin.

2   Your son should train to become an accountant – he's got a very good head for
....

4   I'll hang on to this bottle-opener. It might come in ....

5   I was only sixteen when I first fell head over .... in love.

10 I wasn't expecting a letter from her; it arrived quite out of the ....

11 As son of one of the richest men in Europe he was certainly born with a
.... spoon in his mouth.

12 That wasn't at all what I meant! You've got hold of the wrong end of the
.... again.

13 The robbery went off so smoothly that the police suspected it was an
.... job – that someone in the bank had been an accomplice.

16 "What are your new neighbours like?"
"Oh, they're really friendly. And their children and ours get on like a house
on ...."

17 My new flat's really small – there isn't room to .... a cat in it.

17 Complete the sentences 2

Complete sentences 1–15 by choosing an ending from a–o.

1 The thief couldn't really claim he was innocent because he . . .
2 She got the sack because she . . .
3 They wished me "many happy returns" . . .
4 Don't ask Pauline to do the washing up – she's . . .
5 Since my parents moved to Wales, my visits to them . . .
6 He wore a hat to disguise the fact that he . . .
7 He talked so much that no one . . .
8 James is in a really bad mood this morning. He . . .
9 You'd better pull your socks up if you . . .
10 Let's bury the hatchet and . . .
11 Before he spoke, he asked for a glass of water because he . . .
12 My boss and I don't see eye to eye . . .
13 He hadn't prepared a speech but spoke . . .
14 He was a very timid person who . . .
15 I got into hot water the other day . . .

a . . . was a bit thin on top.
b . . . for borrowing the school record player without permission.
c . . . off the top of his head.
d . . . want to pass the exam.
e . . . had been caught red-handed.
f . . . must have got out of bed the wrong side.
g . . . wouldn't say "boo" to a goose.
h . . . become friends again.
i . . . kept turning up late for work.
j . . . over the new sales campaign.
k . . . all fingers and thumbs.
l . . . could get a word in edgeways.
m . . . on my birthday.
n . . . are very few and far between.
o . . . had a frog in his throat.

Write your answers here:

1	2	3	4	5	6	7	8	9	10	11	12	13	14	15

18 Explain the meaning

Explain the meaning of the idioms in <u>italics</u> in each of the following sentences.

1   He tends to exaggerate, so if I were you I'd *take* everything he says *with a pinch of salt*.

2   Andrew Lloyd-Webber's latest musical *has taken* New York *by storm*.

3   I found it extremely difficult to *hold my tongue* when he started praising the South African government and saying what a marvellous job it was doing.

4   The taxi fare was £3.50. I gave the driver £4 and told him to *keep the change*.

5   I think you'd better phone up your mother to tell her you've arrived safely. It will *set her mind at rest*.

6   James won't do anything without asking his wife first. You can see who *wears the trousers* in that family.

7   My brother was involved in a car accident on the way to work yesterday. Fortunately, he was uninjured, but his car is a complete *write-off*.

8   "Would you like *a nightcap*, Joy?"
    "No, thank you. Alcohol always gives me a headache."

9   I'm sorry, madam, but we can't order that book for you – it's *out of print*.

10   I didn't like caviar and smoked salmon at first. For me they were *an acquired taste*.

11   It's getting very late. I think we ought to *call it a day*.

12   He's going to become Prime Minister one day – you *mark my words*!

13   The owner needed to sell his Jaguar in a hurry, so I *got it for a song* – only £1,000!

14   But you promised, Patrick! How could you *go back on your word*?

15   We're off to a conference on Wednesday, so we're relying on you to *hold the fort* until we get back.

Look at the drawings below and try to work out what the people are saying. Mark the appropriate letter (a–l) in each of the speech bubbles. Choose from the following:

a "The doctor told me to take it easy."

b "I was in such a hurry this morning that I picked up the wife's by mistake."

c "You were saying, Mr Brown, that you were given the sack from the garage . . ."

d "He's as soft as butter, once he realises that you're not going to hurt him."

e "Is this the short cut you were telling me about?"

f "Mirror, Mirror on the wall . . . tell me a little white lie."

g "I'm just turning in. Would you tell the milkman to leave an extra pint?"

h "Why don't you act your age, George? If you're prepared to say 'Sorry' then I'm prepared to say 'I forgive you'."

i "He's been as good as gold, Mrs Jones. We've been playing cowboys and Indians."

j "Yes, I'm on a banana diet again. Why? Does it show?"

k "Hello, I'm Paul. It's my job to get rid of you!"

l "Yes, Susan, I'd love to come round for a chat. Peter won't mind. He said he wanted an early night."

20 Choose the animal

Fill in the missing words from the sentences below. Choose from the following, using plural forms where necessary.

bird	crocodile	goat	lion
bull	dog	goose	pig
cat	donkey	horse	rat
cow	fish	kitten	stag

1   Turning up half an hour late for the interview really cooked his ....

2   We were hoping to keep the wedding a secret, but my mother soon let the .... out of the bag.

3   You're flogging a dead .... trying to get Harry to change his mind!

4   I don't think I'd recognise her now; it's ....'s years since I last saw her.

5   Harold has really gone to the .... since his wife died. Looking at him now, it's hard to believe he was once a successful barrister.

6   It's not that I mind giving her a lift home every Tuesday, but what gets my .... is the fact that she's never once offered to pay for the petrol.

7   As I had to go to Swansea on business, I decided to kill two .... with one stone and visit my old school as well.

8   Although he had only known her for two weeks he decided to take the .... by the horns and ask her to marry him.

9   She loved tennis and could watch it until the .... came home.

10   You're upset now, I know. But you'll soon forget her – after all, there are plenty more .... in the sea.

11   That's the last time I invite Steve for a meal. He really made a .... of himself last night.

12   Don't be fooled. She's not a bit sad; they're just .... tears.

13   When their grandfather died, Robert and his sister got the ....'s share of his money.

14 After years of commuting from Brighton to London, he decided to get out of the .... race and buy a small farm in Wales.

15 When I tell my parents that Paul and I have decided to call off the wedding they're going to have ....

16 We're off to a .... party tonight – David's getting married on Saturday.

21 True or false? 2

Say whether the idioms in the following sentences are used correctly (true) or incorrectly (false).

		TRUE	FALSE
1	My cousin is very strong. He's extremely *tight-fisted*.	[ ]	[ ]
2	The bank manager was arrested for *cooking the books*.	[ ]	[ ]
3	You would probably not be very happy if someone said to you, "You're *a brick*."	[ ]	[ ]
4	To *call the banns* has something to do with politics.	[ ]	[ ]
5	Men are not usually invited to *a hen party*.	[ ]	[ ]
6	To *eavesdrop* is to listen accidentally to a private conversation.	[ ]	[ ]
7	To *grease someone's palm* means to tell his or her fortune.	[ ]	[ ]
8	A travelling salesman often has to *live out of a suitcase*.	[ ]	[ ]
9	He can't read music; he plays the piano *by ear*.	[ ]	[ ]
10	To *lead someone up the garden path* is another way of saying "to get married".	[ ]	[ ]
11	I forgot to phone David – it completely *slipped my mind*.	[ ]	[ ]
12	The pop concert was a disaster. It *went like a bomb*.	[ ]	[ ]
13	I felt really pleased when she told me that she thought I had *a fat chance* of getting the job.	[ ]	[ ]
14	Most people would be pleased if they got a *windfall*.	[ ]	[ ]
15	He spends all his free time body-building. That's why he's so *thick-skinned*.	[ ]	[ ]
16	The policeman saw that I wasn't wearing a seatbelt, but fortunately he *turned a blind eye* to it.	[ ]	[ ]

22 Definitions 3

Match up the definitions on the left (1–16) with the correct idiom on the right (a–p).

1	intelligence, reasoning ability	a	a blessing in disguise
2	something that is extremely easy (to do)	b	a blue-collar worker
3	stealing goods while shopping	c	a dead-end job
4	a story that is so exaggerated or incredible that it is difficult to believe	d	elbow grease
5	something which appears bad at first but then turns out well	e	a false alarm
6	a worker who does an office job	f	grey matter
7	a trick played upon someone	g	a nest-egg
8	a factory worker rather than an office worker	h	a pain in the neck
9	a lot of excitement and discussion about something that is trivial	i	a piece of cake
10	an amount of money saved for future use	j	a practical joke
11	a job without prospects	k	a red-letter day
12	a very important day in someone's life	l	shoplifting
13	a tiresome, irritating person	m	a shot in the dark
14	physical application to hard work	n	a storm in a teacup
15	a wild guess	o	a tall story
16	a warning of danger which turns out to be false	p	a white-collar worker

35

23 Choose the idiom 3

Choose the word or phrase which best completes each sentence.

1 In my opinion, anyone who would risk his life just to climb a mountain must be ....

   a off colour   **b** off his head   **c** the worse for wear
   d long in the tooth

2 He worked at a car factory and usually .... at 7.30 every morning.

   a signed the pledge   **b** called the shots   **c** clocked in
   d opened an account

3 You cut it ....! Another minute and we'd have left without you.

   a fine   **b** short   **c** close   **d** loose

4 Before she left for Australia she promised her parents that she would drop them .... at least once a month.

   a a note   **b** a word   **c** the news   **d** a line

5 I was all set to take the job in Tokyo, but at the last minute I .... and decided to stay in Britain.

   a pulled my finger out   **b** got cold feet   **c** held my horses
   d called it a day

6 Do you mind if I give you my decision tomorrow? I'd like to ....

   a read between the lines   **b** pass the buck   **c** sleep on it
   d take it to heart

7 "What I've got to say to you now is strictly .... and most certainly not for publication," said the government official to the reporter.

   a beside the point   **b** for the time being   **c** by the way
   d off the record

8 You'd better not tease Samantha when she's tired. You know how .... she gets.

   a ratty   **b** sheepish   **c** catty   **d** tipsy

9 The police are working .... with the Football Association in an effort to stamp out soccer violence.

   a hand over fist   **b** hand in hand   **c** hand in glove
   d head over heels

10 I've never really enjoyed going to the ballet or the opera; they're not really my ....

   a piece of cake   **b** chip off the old block   **c** biscuit   **d** cup of tea

11 When the chairman retired he was given a .... of £50,000.

    a consolation prize   **b** golden handshake   **c** blank cheque
    d parting shot

12 Did you see Jonathan this morning? He looked like .... It must have been quite a party last night!

    a a bear with a sore head   **b** death warmed up   **c** a dead duck
    d a wet blanket

13 Although she had never used a word-processor before, she soon got the .... of it.

    a feel   **b** touch   **c** swing   **d** hang

14 "What's wrong with Guy today? He's unusually quiet."
"He's got something on his .... I expect."

    a brain   **b** mind   **c** thoughts   **d** brow

24 Idioms with "on"

Fill in the missing words in the sentences below. Choose from the following:

on account of	on principle	on the contrary	on the run
on and off	on purpose	on the dot	on the shelf
on average	on tenterhooks	on the house	on the spur
on board	on the cards	on the other hand	of the moment
on call	on the carpet	on the rocks	on the whole
on one's toes*			

(* change as appropriate)

1 When I was growing up in Wales, a girl was considered to be .... if she wasn't married by the time she was twenty-five.

2 "The drinks are ....!" said the smiling landlord to his customers on Christmas morning.

3 My mother, being an ardent socialist, disagrees with everything the Conservative Party does ....

4 We mustn't be late tomorrow, so I expect you all to be here at 9 o'clock ....

5 The football match had to be postponed .... the bad weather.

6 James and I hadn't really planned to get married; we just did it .... one day.

7 "How much do teachers earn in your country?"
"It varies, but .... about £1,000 a month."

8 Sales have really fallen off this year. If this goes on much longer, the company will soon be ....

9 His work is quite good ...., but there are still one or two things I'm not really happy with.

10 Arnold has been learning Russian .... for three years.

11 Selling computers is very competitive. You really have to be .... to keep your job.

12 You'll be .... if the boss ever finds out that you forgot to deliver those parcels on time last week.

13 She didn't know whether to take the job or not. On the one hand the salary was much better, but .... it meant a lot more travelling every day.

14 I hate travelling by boat. As soon as I get .... I start to feel seasick.

15 After ten days of being ...., he finally gave himself up to the police.

16 One of the disadvantages of being a doctor is that you are frequently .... at weekends.

17 The students were all .... as they awaited the results of the examination.

18 It isn't true that I hate pop music; .... I like it very much.

19 It's .... that the Foreign Secretary will be forced to resign because of that business in the Middle East.

20 It was no accident! You did it ....!

25 Idioms of comparison 2

Choose the word or phrase which best completes each sentence.

1 He was a natural singer with a voice that was as clear as ....

   a a waterfall   **b** a lake   **c** a bell   **d** a mirror

2 After a good night's sleep he woke up feeling as fresh as .... and eager to start work again.

   a fruit   **b** a daisy   **c** a kitten   **d** a maiden

3 He might look kind and sympathetic, but deep down he's as hard as ....

   a nails   **b** a mountain   **c** a gangster   **d** an iceberg

4 What on earth have you got in this suitcase? It's as heavy as ....!

   a an elephant   **b** lead   **c** concrete   **d** a corpse

5 Pauline can't have emigrated to New Zealand because I saw her last night at Simon's party, as .... as life.

   a true   **b** real   **c** good   **d** large

6 It's no use arguing with him, he won't listen. He's as stubborn as ....

   a a mule   **b** a spoilt child   **c** a strawberry   **d** a trade union

7 "You're drunk!"
"No, I'm not. I'm as sober as ....!"

   a a priest   **b** Sunday   **c** a judge   **d** a Muslim

8 Am I nervous? Of course not. Look at my hand – it's as steady as ....

   a a bridge   **b** a rock   **c** steel bars   **d** a stepladder

9 As students, David, Kevin and William were as thick as ....

   a thieves   **b** boy scouts   **c** a team   **d** thistles

10 Whenever I feel embarrassed I always go as red as ....

   a a rose   **b** lipstick   **c** a raspberry   **d** a beetroot

11 Buying shares in this company is as safe as .... There's no way you can lose your money.

   a a bank   **b** houses   **c** gold bars   **d** a vault

12 She was so tired last night that she slept like .... until 10 o'clock this morning.

    a a squirrel   **b** death   **c** a log   **d** a zombie

13 We'd better get some extra food in if your brother's coming to stay with us. He eats like ....!

    a a lion   **b** a starving man   **c** an eagle   **d** a horse

14 Normally she smoked 15–20 cigarettes a day, but whenever she was worried or nervous she smoked like ....

    a a chimney   **b** a forest fire   **c** a steam engine   **d** a salmon

15 "Is the dress too big?"
"No, not at all. It fits like ...."

    a a mould   **b** a glove   **c** glue   **d** a pillowcase

16 James never remembers anything; he's got a memory like ....

    a cotton wool   **b** a mouse   **c** a sieve   **d** a bucket

17 If your father ever finds out that you've been taking days off school he'll be down on you like a .... of bricks.

    a wheelbarrow   **b** ton   **c** pile   **d** load

18 From the moment they first met they got on like ....

    a two peas in a pod   **b** fish and chips   **c** a house on fire
    d clockwork

19 News of the new pay agreement spread like .... throughout the factory.

    a wildfire   **b** butter   **c** the plague   **d** a flood

20 She was so frightened that she was shaking like ....

    a the wind   **b** a leaf   **c** jelly   **d** a flag

26 Sort out the idioms

Below are 30 idioms, each of which can be associated with one of the headings below. Try to place each idiom under the appropriate heading (3 under each).

at loggerheads	have words
bigheaded	keep one's head above water
browned off	keyed up
down-hearted	long in the tooth
down in the dumps	off colour
Dutch courage	on a shoestring
feather one's nest	on tenterhooks
feel under the weather	out of sorts
fly off the handle	past one's prime
getting on in years	put the wind up someone
go off the deep end	see pink elephants
hair-raising	see red
have a bone to pick with someone	stuck-up
have one's heart in one's mouth	tipsy
have something on one's mind	too big for one's boots

VANITY/CONCEIT

_____

_____

_____

UNHAPPINESS

_____

_____

_____

MONEY

_____

_____

_____

FEAR

_____

_____

_____

ANXIETY/WORRY   ILL-HEALTH

_____   _____
_____   _____
_____   _____

ALCOHOL   ANGER

_____   _____
_____   _____
_____   _____

DISAGREEMENT/ARGUMENT   AGE

_____   _____
_____   _____
_____   _____

Complete the crossword 3

Complete the following crossword.

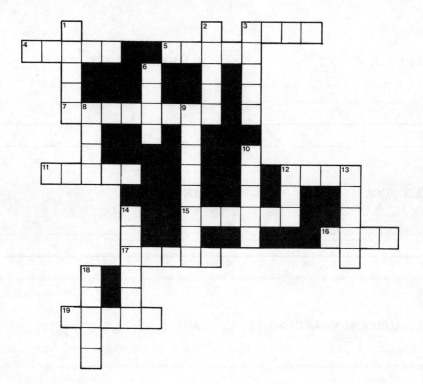

ACROSS

3 Your son seems to be making quite a .... for himself, Mrs Webb. I bet you're proud of him.

4 His arguments sound convincing, but when you examine them closely they just don't hold ....

5 Trying to get Mr Simpson to contribute something to the staff children's party is like trying to get blood out of a ....

7 "What does 'nefarious' mean?"
"I haven't the .... idea. Ask Brian."

11 With a bit of luck, the company should manage to .... even by the end of the year.

12 I don't think we should mention the war in front of your aunt. She suffered a lot so it's best to let sleeping .... lie.

15 It's typical of him to take all the credit when we're the ones who've done all the .... work!

16 Well, if you're not prepared to do anything about it, then I shall just have to go over your .... and speak to the manager.

17 I'm afraid I'm a bit .... of money this month. Do you think you could lend me £30?

19 I'm in two .... whether to go to Spain for the summer or not.

DOWN

1 British people have a reputation for keeping a .... upper lip.

2 I do wish you'd come to the ...., Sally. We haven't got all night, you know.

3 "I'm sorry I'm late."
   "Not to worry. Better late than ...."

6 He failed to get a place at university, and ever since then he's had a .... on his shoulder.

8 I'm telling you .... and for all that unless you work a lot harder, you're not going to pass the exam.

9 I really can't imagine what I've done to offend Carol. I said hello to her but she just gave me the cold ....

10 When he took out a pipe and started smoking it, he got some dirty .... from one or two of his fellow-passengers.

12 "It was a wonderful party after my graduation – a real red-letter ...."

13 No one ever talks about cousin Charles. Apparently, he's the black .... of the family.

14 We were all very sad to hear that her grandmother had .... away during the night.

18 "Oh dear, I hope I haven't hurt his feelings!"
   "No, don't worry. Philip's so ....-skinned he probably thought you were talking about someone else."

28 Choose the part of the body

Fill in the missing words from the sentences below. Choose from the following, using plural forms where necessary.

arm	bone	cheek	foot	heart	nerve
back	brain	chest	hair	leg	stomach
blood	breast	finger	hand	mouth	tooth

1 Being retired, he suddenly found himself with lots of time on his .... but with little to do to occupy it.

2 You need to have a strong .... to work in a slaughterhouse.

3 He got up very late this morning and then had the .... to complain about his breakfast being cold!

4 She had a sweet .... and couldn't resist buying chocolates and cream cakes.

5 None of the students liked Mr Baker. In fact, everyone was glad to see the .... of him when he left to teach in Italy.

6 I think I'll go and stretch my .... I've been sitting down all morning and I'm feeling a bit stiff.

7 I've got an essay to write on the history of computing. Unfortunately, I don't know anything about it, so do you mind if I pick your ....?

8 He used to love mountain-climbing, but when a friend of his was killed in the Himalayas he lost his .... and never went climbing again.

9 The viewers were up in .... when the television station announced it was going to change the time of the evening news broadcast from 9 o'clock to 9.30.

10 There's something wrong somewhere. I can't put my .... on what it is exactly, but something just doesn't feel right.

11 The cruel way some owners treat their pets makes my .... boil.

12 "Hurry up, Dorothy! The taxi's waiting!"
"All right, keep your .... on! I'm coming."

13 Getting a problem off your .... is the first stage to being able to solve it.

14 She decided to make a clean .... of everything and confess that she was the one who had stolen the money.

15 You'd better be careful what you say to Samantha. You know how sensitive she is to criticism – she takes everything to ....

16 I think there's going to be trouble at the meeting tonight; I can feel it in my ....

17 David and the new boss seem to have got off on the wrong .... Poor David! There go his chances for promotion.

18 Stop putting words into my ....! I never said opera was boring, I just said I preferred musicals, that's all.

29 Complete the proverbs 1

Complete the following proverbs by choosing an ending from those marked a–p. Then try to explain what each proverb means.

1 Honesty ...
2 Better late ...
3 Still waters ...
4 Actions ...
5 More haste ...
6 A fool and his money ...
7 All's well ...
8 A rolling stone ...
9 A stitch in time ...
10 Don't count your chickens ...
11 Strike ...
12 Let sleeping dogs ...
13 Look before you ...
14 Once bitten ...
15 Make hay ...
16 Rome ...

a ... less speed.
b ... gathers no moss.
c ... twice shy.
d ... lie.
e ... while the sun shines.
f ... is the best policy.
g ... was not built in a day.
h ... than never.
i ... leap.
j ... are soon parted.
k ... run deep.
l ... that ends well.
m ... while the iron is hot.
n ... before they are hatched.
o ... saves nine.
p ... speak louder than words.

Write your answers here:

1	2	3	4	5	6	7	8	9	10	11	12	13	14	15	16

30 Definitions 4

Match up the definitions on the left (1–16) with the correct idiom on the right (a–p).

1	be in prison	a	be an old hand at something
2	enjoy oneself	b	be out of pocket
3	be experienced	c	break one's word
4	have one's revenge	d	bring something to mind
5	quarrel in public, have a row	e	come to a head
6	look angrily at someone	f	come to light
7	lose money over something	g	do time
8	remain alert	h	get one's own back
9	reach a crisis	i	give someone a black look
10	wait, be patient	j	give someone the slip
11	not keep a promise	k	have a good time
12	become known	l	have one's hands full
13	relax	m	hold one's horses
14	recall, remember something	n	keep on one's toes
15	be very busy	o	make a scene
16	escape from someone (e.g. the police)	p	put one's feet up

Choose the word or phrase which best completes each sentence.

1 That sofa would .... nicely for the living-room.

 a match **b** pass **c** do **d** fit

2 He was wearing very shabby, dirty clothes and looked very ....

 a easy-going **b** down to earth **c** out of shape **d** down at heel

3 Since he started his own business he has been making money hand over
 ....

 a fist **b** heel **c** head **d** palm

4 I can't see us beating them at tennis this year – we're so out of ....

 a step **b** practice **c** fitness **d** breath

5 I wouldn't move there – not for all the ....

 a fish in the sea **b** sand in the Sahara **c** guns in Texas
 d tea in China

6 I'm not surprised Colin's ill. He's been .... for a long time. It was
 bound to affect his health sooner or later.

 a having his cake and eating it **b** burning the candle at both ends
 c playing with fire **d** going to town

7 I just couldn't remember her name even though it was on the .... of
 my tongue.

 a edge **b** tip **c** top **d** front

8 She was in such a hurry in the morning that she put her jumper on
 ....

 a sideways **b** upside-down **c** inside out **d** off the cuff

9 That's exactly what I mean, Ben. You've .... !

 a put your foot in it **b** killed two birds with one stone
 c put two and two together **d** hit the nail on the head

10 "I'm going for an interview for a job this afternoon."
 "Good luck! I'll keep my .... crossed for you."

 a legs **b** fingers **c** arms **d** hands

11 "If only I hadn't lent him all that money!"
 "Well you did, so it's no good crying over .... milk."

 a spilt **b** wasted **c** sour **d** goat's

12 It's not surprising that he became a writer because he always longed to see his name ....

    a in type   **b** in print   **c** in letters   **d** in edition

13 The car swerved to avoid a cyclist and just missed hitting a pedestrian by ....

    a a slight edge   **b** a narrow escape   **c** a close thing
    d a hair's breadth

14 Well, well, if it isn't Kathy Lewis! You're a sight for .... eyes!

    a old   **b** blue   **c** sore   **d** crocodile

15 I know times have been bad lately, Peter, but keep your .... up; things are bound to get better soon.

    a chin   **b** head   **c** socks   **d** mind

What are they saying?   3

Look at the drawings below and try to work out what the people are saying.
Mark the appropriate letter (a–l) in each of the speech bubbles. Choose from
the following:

a   "I'd better come with you. I've been cooking the books."
b   "Of course she's got butterflies in her stomach. It's her first marriage."
c   "You're fired, Biggs. You too, Miss Jones."
d   "I think someone wants us to get a move on."
e   "Keep this under your hat, Sally – my husband has a drink problem."
f   "To be honest, Charles, I'm scared stiff of the thought of retirement."
g   "Stop being so self-conscious, darling. Lots of men are a bit thin on top."
h   "When I get out of here I'm going to paint the town red with that £15 I
    stole 25 years ago."
i   "Who got out of bed on the wrong side this morning, then?"
j   "Your drinks machine seems to be out of order."
k   "But how much are we in the red?"
l   "I'm afraid we only have a skeleton staff at the moment."

33 Idioms with "by", "for", "off" and "out of"

Fill in the missing words in the sentences below. Choose from the following:

by chance	for good	off and on	out of bounds
by far	for short	off duty	out of breath
by hand	for the high	off the beaten	out of hand
by heart	jump	track	out of the
by no means	for the time	off the top of	question
by the way	being	one's head*	out of tune
for a change			

(* change as appropriate)

1 I'm fed up with doing the same thing every weekend. Let's go away somewhere ....

2 He lived in a small cottage which, because it was ...., was very difficult to find.

3 I think I'd better give up smoking. I was completely .... this morning after climbing two flights of stairs.

4 It is .... unusual in some countries for a family to have two cars.

5 The demonstration got .... and quickly developed into a full-scale battle between the demonstrators and the police.

6 The government has decided to shelve its plans to raise the school leaving age to eighteen – at least ....

7 These things are more expensive because they're all made ....

8 She said she would join us at the restaurant later; when she was ....

9 ...., did you remember to post that letter I gave you yesterday?

10 We can't use this piano, it's ....

11 He wasn't prepared for the question, so he was forced to answer ....

12 Of all the houses we've looked at, this one is .... the best.

13 The pupils were not allowed to go to the local fish and chip shop during their lunch hour. It was .... to them.

14 My sister has been living in Ireland .... for the past seven years.

15 If the government puts up income tax again I shall leave this country .... and go and live in Spain or Greece.

16 I'm afraid I can't let you have next week off, Miss Blake. It's quite ....; we have far too much to do at the moment.

17 Do you like my ring? I saw it quite .... in the window of an antique shop while I was shopping in the Old Town.

18   His name was Benjamin, but he was called Ben ....

19   Mr Wilson's .... He's been caught fiddling the accounts.

20   Probably the only really effective way of learning prepositions is to learn them ....

34 **Complete the proverbs** **2**

Complete the following proverbs by choosing an ending from those marked
a–p. Then try to explain what each proverb means.

1 Absence ...
2 Beauty ...
3 First come, ...
4 When the cat's away ...
5 No news ...
6 A miss ...
7 One good turn ...
8 A bird in the hand ...
9 A bad workman ...
10 Charity ...
11 Practice ...
12 Necessity ...
13 A new broom ...
14 One man's meat ...
15 Too many cooks ...
16 Where there's a will ...

a ... is worth two in the bush.
b ... begins at home.
c ... is as good as a mile.
d ... spoil the broth.
e ... is the mother of invention.
f ... makes the heart grow fonder.
g ... always blames his tools.
h ... sweeps clean.
i ... there's a way.
j ... is only skin deep.
k ... the mice will play.
l ... deserves another.
m ... first served.
n ... makes perfect.
o ... is good news.
p ... is another man's poison.

Write your answers here:

1	2	3	4	5	6	7	8	9	10	11	12	13	14	15	16

35 True or false 3

Say whether the idioms in the following sentences are used correctly (true) or incorrectly (false).

		TRUE	FALSE
1	He goes there often – at least *once in a blue moon*.	[ ]	[ ]
2	He didn't have much power; he was only a *figurehead*.	[ ]	[ ]
3	He liked her a lot; he *had* a real *soft spot for her*.	[ ]	[ ]
4	It's not new; it's *second-rate*.	[ ]	[ ]
5	He couldn't go any faster; he was already *going flat out*.	[ ]	[ ]
6	He's an extremely good talker. He really does *have the gift of the gab*.	[ ]	[ ]
7	My grandmother has been married for fifty years and she's still a very happy *old maid*.	[ ]	[ ]
8	My uncle's busy at the moment in the garden; he's *pushing up daisies*. Can I take a message?	[ ]	[ ]
9	I don't understand it; it's *all Greek to me*.	[ ]	[ ]
10	You would probably feel very proud if someone *gave you the sack*.	[ ]	[ ]
11	He was so hungry that he *ate his heart out*.	[ ]	[ ]
12	A company car and luncheon vouchers are just two of the *perks* you get when you work here.	[ ]	[ ]
13	We ate *potatoes in their jackets* last night.	[ ]	[ ]
14	He loved animals and spent a lot of his free time *in the doghouse*.	[ ]	[ ]
15	This book is *dog-eared*. I can't possibly sell it.	[ ]	[ ]
16	He loves gardening; he's very *weedy*.	[ ]	[ ]

36 Rewrite the sentences 2

For each of the sentences below write a new sentence with a similar meaning. Substitute the words in underlined italics with the word in CAPITAL LETTERS plus one of the verbs in the box. (You may need to use some of them more than once.)

call	come	do	get	give	go	have	keep	lose	pull	put	take

1 *Telephone me* if you feel like going out for a meal one day next week.
RING

....

2 That wasn't what I meant at all! You've *completely misunderstood me* as usual!
STICK

....

3 *There's no need for us to hurry*; the play doesn't start until 7.30.
TIME

....

4 The fact that the President had been a drug addict *was not revealed* until several years after his death.
LIGHT

....

5 I may not come first in the race, but I'll *try as hard as I can* not to come last.
BEST

....

6 My husband *is obsessed with football*; it's the only thing he ever thinks about.
BRAIN

....

7 We're organising a going-away party for Sue on Saturday. But *don't tell her* as it's supposed to be a surprise.
QUIET

....

8 If things go wrong, James, whatever you do, don't *panic*.
HEAD

....

9 More than 1,000 runners *participated* in this year's Manchester marathon.
PART

....

10 The way he took everything she did for granted really *annoyed her*.
BACK

....

11 The personnel officer *promised him* that she wouldn't tell anyone that he had been in prison.
WORD

....

12 We'd get the job finished much quicker if everyone *worked as hard as everyone else*.
WEIGHT

....

13 If you don't like the idea then just say so. I believe you should *always speak frankly*.
SPADE

....

14 My father's going to *be really angry* when he finds out that I've lost the car keys.
WALL

....

15 Don't *pay any attention to* what he says; he's only trying to annoy you.
NOTICE

....

Complete the crossword 4

Complete the following crossword by finding one word for each of the idioms in italics.

ACROSS

1 You'd better ask your father if you can borrow the car this time; you know what a *song and dance* he made last time.

6 I can't stand the new boss; he's always *finding fault with* my work.

7 They all looked so nice that I couldn't *make up my mind* which one to buy.

8 Don't expect Tom to buy you a drink, he's far too *tight-fisted*.

9 Don't ask me to do anything else tonight – I'm *all in*.

12 Make yourself at home, Jill, I'll be with you in a *tick*.

13 There's always a *racket* at that market on Saturday morning.

16 She was really *down in the dumps* when she didn't get that job – she'd set her heart on it.

18 "You look tired, Joanna."
"Yes, I am. All I want to do tonight is *put my feet up*."

22 It wasn't an accident at all – she did it *on purpose*. I saw her!

23 My visits to my old school are very *few and far between* nowadays.

25 His speech was interesting but a lot of what he said was *off the point*. He should have kept more to the main subject.

26 That dog of theirs really *put the wind up* me. I honestly didn't think we'd get out of there in one piece.

DOWN

2 Her husband has been *out of work* since 1986.

3 No, put your money away. The drinks are *on the house* tonight.

4 We can't really let the new boy do it – he's far too *green*.

5 Everything seems to be *above board*, but there's something that doesn't feel quite right. I just wish I knew what it was.

10 Seeing as they're both teachers, it's not surprising really that their children are *brainy*.

11 Would you two *get a move on*; we haven't got all night!

14 The holiday was an *out and out* disaster. Everything went wrong from start to finish.

15 Well, that's another £10 *down the drain*. That's the last time I put a bet on a horse.

17 That car I bought from your brother is *a dead loss*. It's been in and out of the garage at least twenty times since I bought it.

19 They left the restaurant leaving me to *foot the bill*.

20 Although they have been working on the problem for weeks, they still haven't made very much *headway*.

21 "I think it's a lot harder for a woman to combine a career and a family than it is for a man."
"I *beg to differ*! There's absolutely no difference whatsoever."

24 She must be *off her head* to turn down the chance of a month's free holiday to the West Indies.

38 Choose the adjective

Fill in the missing adjectives in the sentences below. Choose from the following:

bated	flat	pet	square
broad	foregone	practical	tall
confirmed	golden	rough	unwritten
dark	hot	sharp	weak
fair	naked	sore	wishful

1   She had a very .... tongue, and could be really sarcastic when she was angry.

2   The result of the election was a/an .... conclusion. Everyone knew which party would win.

3   There is a/an .... law in this club that you never borrow money from a fellow-member.

4   She had a very vivid imagination but her spelling was her .... point when it came to writing essays.

5   You don't need a telescope to see the planet Venus – you can see it with the .... eye.

6   Watch out for Paul Blake in the competition; he's a bit of a/an .... horse.

7   We decided to play a/an .... joke on our teacher by putting a "For Sale" sign on his car.

8   Don't mention last year's Christmas party to Harry; it's a bit of a/an .... point with him.

9   The one thing about Pamela is that you can trust her; you know she'll give you a/an .... deal.

10   He'll never get married; he's a/an .... bachelor.

11   Don't believe a word he says; it's just another of his .... stories.

12   Do you know if there's a/an .... line between 10 Downing Street and the Kremlin?

13   I don't really want to be twenty again; it was just .... thinking.

14   The competitors waited with .... breath for the results to be read out.

15   The robbery was committed in .... daylight.

16   "How many were there at the meeting last night?"
"I'm not sure exactly, but at a/an .... guess I'd say about three hundred."

17   One of his .... hates was people pushing in front of him at bus stops.

18 I was late for work this morning because my car had a .... tyre.

19 This is a .... opportunity for you, Tom. You must take it.

20 It was the first .... meal the tramp had had in days.

39 Find someone . . .

Look at the drawings below. Find someone:

a   who has been caught
    red-handed.   [ ]
b   who has been pipped at the
    post.   [ ]
c   who has just hit the sack.   [ ]
d   who has just named the day. [ ]
e   who is a blackleg.   [ ]
f   who is behind the times. [ ]
g   who is having a whale of a
    time.   [ ]

h   who is in the limelight.   [ ]
i   who is keeping fit.   [ ]
j   who is light-fingered.   [ ]
k   who is on duty.
l   who is out of condition.   [ ]
m   who is roughing it.   [ ]
n   who is run off his/her feet. [ ]
o   who is showing off.   [ ]
p   who is taking to his/her
    heels.   [ ]

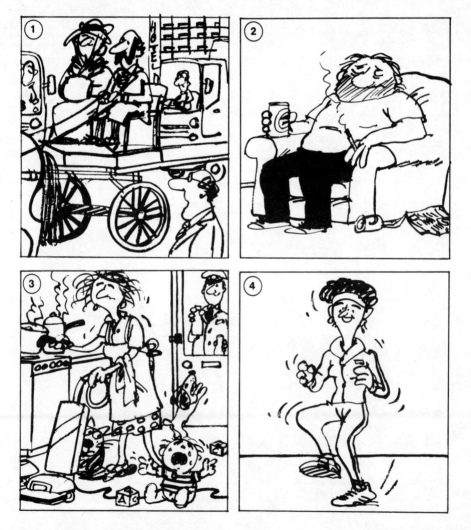

64

67

40 Paired idioms

Complete the paired idioms in the sentences below. Choose from the following:

about	front	sound	tear
blood	large	span	thin
bull	nail	square	thumbs
cons	shoulders	sweet	tired
fast	soul	take	void

1 She was an outstanding student whose work was head and .... above the others in her class.

2 The lecture was just the way the students liked it – short and ....

3 Although it has its faults, by and .... Britain is a pretty good country to live in.

4 Don't ask James to do anything practical; he's all fingers and ....

5 Pauline was so funny on Saturday. She really was the life and .... of the party.

6 England were beaten fair and .... by the West Indies in the Third Test at Lords.

7 He's not feeling well at the moment, but he should be up and .... again in a few days.

8 The contract was declared null and .... as one of the partners had forgotten to sign it.

9 You didn't believe what he said, did you? It was just another one of his cock and .... stories!

10 Oh, thank heavens you're both safe and ....! I was so worried about you.

11 They promised to stand by each other through thick and ....

12 The carpet in the hall gets a lot of wear and ...., so it's best not to buy anything too expensive.

13 You can't throw him out, surely? Not your brother; not your own flesh and ....!

14 A certain amount of give and .... is essential in any relationship.

15 His flat was so spick and .... that it looked more like a well-kept museum than a home.

16 I'm afraid you'll have to wear a tie, sir. It's a hard and .... rule of the club.

17 They're always fighting tooth and .... I'm surprised they don't get divorced.

18 I couldn't understand why everyone was laughing until I realised that I had my jumper on back to ....

19 The managing director outlined the pros and .... of the proposed merger.

20 I don't know about you, David, but I'm sick and .... of hearing about his 'fantastic' children.

41 Definitions 5

Match up the definitions on the left (1–16) with the correct idiom on the right (a–p).

1 incite someone to do something that perhaps they should not do

2 make a serious effort to improve one's work

3 live from day to day, often without regular money

4 hear a rumour

5 find faults or mistakes in something (e.g. an argument)

6 go from a bad situation to one that is even worse

7 flatter someone (often in order to get something)

8 become angry

9 challenge someone to do what he or she has threatened to do (usually because one does not believe the person will do it)

10 be humiliated or be made to look foolish in front of others

11 make a mistake, have the wrong idea of something

12 annoy or irritate someone

13 speak angrily to someone

14 wait patiently for a suitable opportunity to do something

15 help someone

16 completely ignore a person while passing him or her

a bark up the wrong tree

b bide one's time

c butter someone up

d call someone's bluff

e cut someone dead

f egg someone on

g hear something on the grapevine

h jump down someone's throat

i jump out of the frying pan into the fire

j lend someone a hand

k live from hand to mouth

l lose face

m lose one's temper

n pick holes in something

o pull one's socks up

p rub someone up the wrong way

42 Prepositions and particles

Fill in the missing prepositions or particles in the following sentences.

1   Help! Help! My house is .... fire!

2   Paul won't do anything without asking his wife first. She's really got him .... her thumb.

3   The thing I don't like about my present job is that we often have to work up to ten hours .... a stretch.

4   If you have any complaints, then tell me .... my face. I can't stand people who do things .... my back.

5   My mother never gives anyone a tip .... principle.

6   .... you, me and the gatepost, I don't think the new boss will last more than a few months.

7   This work is taking much longer than I thought. .... this rate it'll be Christmas before it's finished.

8   This piano was a present from my grandmother and I wouldn't part with it .... love or money.

9   The party was already .... full swing by the time they got there.

10   He didn't have time to prepare a speech so he had to give one .... the cuff.

11   Throughout the flight he was very much .... edge, and didn't start to relax until the plane had landed.

12   I wouldn't like to be .... her shoes when Miss Brown finds out that she's lost the exam papers.

13   I'd love to come to the concert with you but I can't, I'm afraid. I'm .... my ears in work this week.

14   It was supposed to be a surprise present, but Yvonne gave the game .... by asking him if he'd bought John Fowles' latest novel.

15   Playing squash once a week was his way of letting .... steam.

16   The speech was so moving that he began to feel a lump .... his throat.

17   You should taste their smoked salmon. Honestly, Paula, it's .... this world!

18   "I think Arsenal are the best football club in Britain."
     "Come .... it! What about Liverpool, then?"

43 Choose the colour

Complete the idioms below with a suitable colour. Choose from the box.
(You will need to use some words more than once.)

black	green	red
blue	grey	white
brown	pink	yellow

1   In most countries, goods that are scarce are usually freely available on the
.... market – provided you have the money to pay for them.

2   You can argue with her until you're .... in the face, but once she's
made up her mind she won't listen to you, no matter what you say.

3   After several weeks of discussions, the group were given the ....
light, and could finally go ahead with the new project.

4   There's no point in asking my boss for a day off next week. I'm in her
.... books at the moment so she's bound to say no.

5   She had only recently had lunch with her cousin, so the news of his death
came as a bolt from the ....

6   Although we got a lot of nice wedding presents, we also got one or two
.... elephants.

7   There is a common prejudice that girls who are very beautiful must
automatically be lacking in .... matter – so-called 'dumb blondes'.

8   Next Friday is a ....-letter day for my sister and her husband; it's
their 25th wedding anniversary.

9   After sunbathing for two hours every day, Joanna was as .... as a
berry.

10   The managing director's reference to the forthcoming sales conference was a
.... herring. He just wanted to get off the subject of this month's poor
sales figures.

11   She went as .... as a sheet when she heard about the accident.

12   If there was a war, I don't think I'd fight. I've got too much of a ....
streak. I'd be terrified of getting killed.

13   I'm sorry, James, I refuse to believe it unless you can show it to me in
.... and ....!

14   Ever since Tom got that huge order with Saudi Arabia he's been the boss's
....................-eyed boy.

15   Don't mention the present government in front of my father; it's like a
.... rag to a bull.

16   I was .... with envy when my neighbour drove up in a brand-new
Jaguar.

17 By the way, Joyce, my husband was tickled .... at your asking him to judge the flower show.

18 For some reason, Swedish films are often synonymous with .... films, which is very strange as there is relatively little pornography in Sweden.

19 Sometimes it is better to tell a .... lie than to hurt someone's feelings.

20 My wife always goes bright .... whenever she gets embarrassed.

44 Newspaper headlines 2

Fill in the missing words in the following newspaper headlines. Choose from the following, making any changes that may be necessary. (The words in brackets under each headline should help you.)

AT LARGE	IN THE BAG	TOE THE LINE
BROKEN-HEARTED	IN THE BALANCE	TURN OVER A
EAT ONE'S WORDS	LAY OFF	NEW LEAF
FROM SCRATCH	ON THE CARDS	UNDER WAY
HUSH MONEY	POP THE QUESTION	UP TO SCRATCH
IN DEEP WATER	SHELVE	WHITE PAPER
IN ONE'S BIRTHDAY	SPILL THE BEANS	WHOLE-HEARTED
SUIT		

NEW SUMMIT MEETING ① **_____ THIS SUMMER**

(likely, possible)

DRUGS SCANDAL TENNIS STAR VOWS TO _____ ②

(reform)

CRITICS UNANIMOUS – LATEST LLOYD-WEBBER MUSICAL NOT _____ ③

(up to the usual standard)

IBM EXECUTIVE _____ ④ **OVER ALLEGED BRIBES**

(in trouble)

LEAD SINGER OF IRISH POP GROUP MARGARINE _____ ⑤

(makes a proposal of marriage, asks someone to marry him)

BRITISH RAIL MAY HAVE TO _____ 1,500 WORKERS ⑥

(dismiss temporarily)

FAMOUS TV-STAR _____ AFTER SON'S DEATH ⑦

(very sad)

NEW EDUCATION BILL GETS _____ SUPPORT FROM OPPOSITION ⑧

(complete, total)

POP STAR APPEARS ON BALCONY _____ ⑨

(naked)

EX MI5 AGENT THREATENS TO _____ ⑩

(reveal everything he knows)

PRIME MINISTER FORCED TO _____ ⑪

(admit he/she was wrong)

RESULT OF TOMORROW'S CUP FINAL _____ ⑫

(certain)

LATEST _____ SHOWS THAT ALCOHOLISM AMONG YOUNG PEOPLE IS ON THE INCREASE ⑬

(government report)

COLD-BLOODED MURDERER STILL _____ ⑭

(free, not caught)

SITE FOR WINTER OLYMPIC GAMES STILL _____ ⑮

(undecided, uncertain)

UNION LEADER PERSUADES MILITANT MEMBERS TO _____ ⑰

(obey orders, do as they are told)

BANKRUPT MILLIONAIRE SAYS HE IS NOT AFRAID TO START _____ ⑱

(right from the beginning again)

LOCAL COUNCIL _____ PLANS FOR NEW SPORTS CENTRE ⑯

(postpones)

WORK ON THE NEW TUNNEL _____ AT LAST ⑲

(progressing)

POLICE OFFICIALS ADMIT TO RECEIVING _____ ⑳

(bribes)

75

45 Word association

Each of the idioms on the left (1–18) can be associated with one of the words or phrases on the right (a–r). Try to match them up.

1	a bottleneck	a	a husband
2	a picket line	b	a party
3	armed to the teeth	c	a job interview
4	behind bars	d	It's a trick!
5	break the ice	e	buying a second-hand car
6	do wonders	f	too many cars
7	Dutch courage	g	an idea
8	henpecked	h	I can't sing!
9	in a cold sweat	i	on strike
10	in a flash	j	authority
11	long-winded	k	a doctor
12	mind one's p's and q's	l	soldiers
13	on call	m	a debate
14	on the level	n	a prisoner
15	out of tune	o	a speech
16	pull the wool over someone's eyes	p	going to prison
17	put one's foot down	q	alcohol
18	take the floor	r	this medicine

Write your answers here:

1	2	3	4	5	6	7	8	9	10	11	12	13	14	15	16	17	18

46 Choose the idiom 5

Choose the word or phrase which best completes each sentence.

1 He may be shy now, but he'll soon come out of his .... when he meets the right girl.

  a shoe   **b** shell   **c** shed   **d** hole

2 It's true, I tell you! I got it from the .... My sister works at the Town Hall. She's the one who made the decision!

  a nag's head   **b** cat's whiskers   **c** horse's mouth
  d lion's den

3 Just look at the way he goes round giving people orders. He's getting a bit too big for his ...., if you ask me.

  a boots   **b** braces   **c** trousers   **d** brains

4 I'm afraid you've caught me on the .... I wasn't expecting you until this afternoon.

  a stove   **b** grapevine   **c** spot   **d** hop

5 Nagging Susan because she smokes too much has no effect on her whatsoever – it's like water off ....

  a a windmill   **b** a duck's back   **c** a dripping tap
  d an umbrella

6 Why don't we have potatoes in their .... tonight for a change?

  a sleeves   **b** shells   **c** jackets   **d** coats

7 Have you seen the new boss? She's the .... image of Marilyn Monroe.

  a live   **b** true   **c** spitting   **d** same

8 He's one of the few .... composers we have in this country.

  a budding   **b** blooming   **c** growing   **d** promised

9 Writing rhymes for birthday cards is really easy. It's money for old ....

  a rags   **b** bread   **c** rope   **d** rubbish

10 Of course you won't become more intelligent if you eat a lot of fish – that's just an old .... tale.

  a maids'   **b** ladies'   **c** mothers'   **d** wives'

11 The day after the office party, Jack had a terrible .... and couldn't bear the slightest noise.

    a hangover   **b** conscience   **c** feeling   **d** anxiety

12 I agree that this is a bit of a .... shot, but we're desperate – we have to do something to try to save the company.

    a hot   **b** long   **c** wild   **d** high

13 We looked in every .... and cranny for the missing ring, but we couldn't find it anywhere.

    a nook   **b** gap   **c** hole   **d** niche

14 I like my new job; the only fly in the .... is the fact that I have to work every other weekend.

    a fat   **b** porridge   **c** soup   **d** ointment

15 It's a .... shame that so little is done nowadays to help the homeless in our large cities.

    a sweeping   **b** crying   **c** dying   **d** pitying

16 My aunt is a bit of a wet .... – she's always spoiling everyone's fun.

    a rag   **b** sheep   **c** rat   **d** blanket

17 There were loud .... from the audience when the compere announced that the main group were unable to perform because of illness.

    a outcry   **b** wolf whistles   **c** catcalls   **d** hoots

18 He just wanted one .... before settling down and getting married.

    a final fling   **b** last leap   **c** happy hop   **d** joyful jump

19 He had a soft .... for his niece and thoroughly spoilt her.

    a heart   **b** way   **c** smile   **d** spot

20 Everyone bosses me about at work; I'm nothing but a ....

    a lame duck   **b** general dogsbody   **c** blue-eyed boy
    d marked man

Answers

TEST 1

1	e	brainy	9	f	cheeky
2	k	nosy	10	m	pigheaded
3	o	well off	11	b	bedridden
4	h	heartless	12	g	hair-raising
5	n	thick	13	c	bigheaded
6	p	wet behind the ears	14	i	keyed up
7	j	long in the tooth	15	l	off colour
8	a	all thumbs	16	d	black and blue all over

TEST 2

1 b **splitting** (The person has a very painful or severe headache)
2 c **beating** (If you "beat about the bush" you tend to avoid saying directly what you mean)
3 a **off the peg** (This is the opposite of being measured up for a dress, jacket, etc. Off the peg clothes usually come in standard sizes only)
4 b **chip in** (This means to contribute money – usually to get a present for someone)
5 c **bucket** (To "bucket down" is to rain very heavily)
6 a **hit the roof** (He got very angry)
7 c **nose** (To "pay through the nose" for something is to pay far more for something than it is really worth)
8 d **teeth** ("By the skin of one's teeth" means the person only just caught the last bus; he or she almost missed it)
9 b **a song** (If something "goes for a song" it is sold very cheaply)
10 d **leg** (To "pull someone's leg" is to tease someone)
11 c **jumping** (The taxi driver pulled away before the traffic lights had changed completely to green; he didn't wait for the traffic lights to change to green)
12 a **broke** (The person doesn't have any money)
13 d **apple** (Her son was very precious to her)
14 b **butterflies** (This means you get nervous)
15 c **hot cakes** (They sell very well or very quickly)

TEST 3

1 **at all costs** (Without fail)
2 **at fault** (It is difficult to know who is to blame)
3 **at the crack of dawn** (Very early)
4 **at most** (The worst or most severe punishment will be a small fine)
5 **at a loose end** (If you have nothing to do this weekend)
6 **at death's door** (Seriously ill; about to die)
7 **at her wits' end** (She was in such a state of anxiety that she didn't know what to do)
8 **at a loss** (Unable to explain the sudden fall in share prices)
9 **at first sight** (It was love from the first moment they saw each other)
10 **at a standstill** (The traffic was not moving)
11 **at sixes and sevens** (Everything is very confused and muddled)
12 **at least** (If nothing else)
13 **at a pinch** (Four if necessary, but with some difficulty)
14 **at all hours** (She is out all the time)
15 **at best** (£250 would be the best price the person could get)
16 **at once** (Immediately)
17 **at loggerheads** (They are always quarrelling)
18 **at will** (It can change the colour of its skin whenever it wants to)
19 **at (such) short notice** (With such little advance warning)
20 **at random** (Without choosing carefully or deliberately)

TEST 4

1 e (He easily forgets things)
2 j (The person is depressed)
3 f (She listens eagerly to everything – even to things that are none of her business)
4 k (He is very lively)
5 b (It doesn't look as though it will stop raining)
6 h (A day when things go wrong)
7 a (She has a very severe or painful headache)

8 d (You always "catch" a cold)
9 l (To "lose your tongue" means to say nothing – often because of shyness or nervousness)
10 i (Help me)
11 g (Jack has always been good at gardening)
12 c ("Isn't there another job you could do?")

TEST 5

Across
1 bone (He is going to complain to you about something)
2 going (I'm just going to the toilet)
6 pressed (I don't have very much time)
9 bachelor (A man who has decided never to get married)
10 tail (I can't understand it at all)
13 tongue (I know the word but I can't quite remember it)
14 nerves (It began to irritate her)
15 catch (I tried to attract the waiter's attention)
18 skin (It's very thin)
19 tree (Map or plan of a family showing the relationships between the various members – parents, children, cousins, etc.)

Down
1 blood (He killed her deliberately and callously; it was planned)
3 night (A "night owl" is someone who likes to stay up late at night)
4 hearing (I'm slightly deaf)
5 status (A possession that shows others that you have money or position)
7 bear (She's very irritable)
8 flying (She passed very easily with good grades)
11 straight (They found it hard not to laugh)
12 second (No, I'll change my mind and have a shandy instead of a beer)
16 hair (Keep calm! Don't get angry!)
17 make (You shouldn't laugh or make jokes about the way he speaks English)

TEST 6

1 f (She was feeling depressed, unhappy)
2 j (He didn't have much money this month)
3 g (We decided to hurry)
4 n (We were exhausted)
5 l (She got caught in a long line of cars)
6 o (She asked me to wait)
7 a (I promised not to tell anyone else about it)
8 k (He finds it hard to live on the money he gets)
9 e (He plays everything instinctively from memory of the tune)
10 d (I was feeling slightly ill)
11 m (We decided to make the time pass more quickly by going into a pub)
12 b (Her name sounds very familiar; I've heard her name before)
13 i (There wasn't a sound anywhere)
14 c (He is very forgetful)
15 h (If you make use of all your opportunities; if you act cleverly or shrewdly)

TEST 7

1 b **the grave** (It's very quiet)
2 c **rain** (He'll be completely well again)
3 a **dog** (I was very sick)
4 d **a horse** (He's very strong)
5 b **rake** (You're very thin)
6 b **old boots** (It's very tough)
7 a **a sheet** (She became very pale)
8 c **a cucumber** (He always remains very calm)
9 b **a post** (He is deaf; he can't hear a thing)
10 c **chalk from cheese** (They are very different)
11 a **ditchwater** (It was extremely boring)
12 b **a fiddle** (I feel very fit and healthy)
13 c **a lamb** (He's very gentle)
14 b **gold** (They've been very well behaved)
15 c **a feather** (It's very light)
16 d **sin** (She's been very miserable)
17 b **the hills** (It's a very old joke)

18 c **the nose on your face** (It's very obvious to everyone)
19 a **punch** (She was very pleased)
20 b **mustard** (We're all very keen)

TEST 8

1	drive	11	tell	21	do
2	hold	12	lead	22	keep
3	run	13	fall	23	catch
4	put	14	change	24	draw
5	use	15	work	25	set
6	bear	16	call	26	lay
7	break	17	chair	27	resist
8	earn	18	beg	28	waste
9	lose	19	throw	29	play
10	drop	20	foot	30	pay

TEST 9

1	HIGH AND LOW	7	WORK TO RULE	12	GETS OUT OF HAND
2	FOR THE HIGH JUMP	8	BLACKOUT	13	ALL THE RAGE
3	ON THE DOLE	9	A FLASH IN THE PAN	14	CAUGHT IN THE ACT
4	GETS COLD FEET	10	MAKE A FLYING VISIT	15	MAKE A COMEBACK
5	GET THE CHOP	11	FROSTY	16	COME INTO FORCE
6	NECK AND NECK				

TEST 10

1 True
2 False (If someone is "browned off", he or she is feeling fed up or bored)
3 True (A dog that is "house-trained" goes out to empty its bowels)
4 True
5 False (A "light-fingered" person is someone who often steals things)
6 False (Most people wouldn't like to be called "proud" or "conceited")
7 True
8 True
9 False (It means to produce favourable results e.g. a project, idea)
10 True (It means my cousin died)
11 False (To "drop off" is to fall asleep)
12 False (To "live in an ivory tower" is to isolate yourself from the rest of the world; to cut yourself off from everyday problems)
13 True
14 True (They don't usually take any risks)
15 True (You can hitch-hike)
16 False (Very few people would like to be tricked or deceived by someone)

TEST 11

1	e	capital punishment	7	k	a gatecrasher	12	d	a brainwave
2	l	a nightcap	8	o	a snag	13	g	a godsend
3	f	a catnap	9	h	a downpour	14	p	a wild goose chase
4	j	a flash in the pan	10	c	a blackleg	15	i	an eyesore
5	n	a scapegoat	11	m	red tape	16	b	a black spot
6	a	a bighead						

TEST 12

1 c **close** (A number of narrow escapes – the person has almost had an accident on several occasions)
2 b **a bee** (He was obsessed with the idea that eating fried meat caused cancer)
3 a **a brick** (To "drop a brick" is to do or say something which is tactless or which causes embarrassment)
4 d **trumpet** (He is always boasting)
5 b **tooth and nail** (He fought fiercely)
6 a **a rat** (To "smell a rat" is to become suspicious; to suspect that something is wrong)
7 d **daggers** (She gave the shop assistant an angry look; she looked angrily at the shop assistant)
8 c **back of his hand** (He knows Hastings really well)
9 c **drain** (It was £800 wasted)
10 a **tight-fisted** (Mean with money)

11 d **hold water** (The rationale of the argument isn't adequate)
12 b **last straw** (The final problem or difficulty in a series of problems which, in this case, led to the person quitting his/her job)
13 d **flies** (He easily loses his temper)
14 b **on my plate** (I have far too much work to do at the moment)
15 d **in a nutshell** (Briefly)

TEST 13

1 (nothing) **in common** (They do not share e.g. hobbies, interests, taste in music, etc.)
2 **in vain** (Without success)
3 **in stock** (Available for sale)
4 **in succession** (Three consecutive years without a break e.g. 1988, 1989, 1990)
5 **in turns** (They shared the coffee making equally, each person doing it on a particular day)
6 **in the dark** (We are not being told; it is being kept secret)
7 **in the nick of time** (At the last possible moment)
8 **in the limelight** (The focus of attention)
9 **in charge of** (Responsible for)
10 **in the red** (I still owe the bank money)
11 **in season** (The time when plants and fruit are normally ripe)
12 **in due course** (At some future date)
13 **in a rut** (In a job or way of life which is boring and which has no prospects of change)
14 **in tune** (Sounds at the correct pitch; sounding well together)
15 **In short** (Briefly; in a few words)
16 **in favour of** (Who support capital punishment)
17 **in cash** (Ready money as opposed to a cheque or a credit card)
18 **in the long run** (In the end; over a long period of time)
19 **in one ear and out the other** (She never listens to anything you say to her)
20 **in theory** (The opposite of "in practice"; an idea which seems fine on paper may not necessarily work out in practice)

TEST 14

1 fell head over heels in love
2 the short list
3 in my shoes
4 have a leg to stand on
5 laughing his/her head off
6 pulling a few strings
7 bring the house down
8 pull yourself together
9 give it a good hiding
10 tell me off
11 sleep like a log
12 get a word in edgeways
13 put it to sleep
14 strike while the iron is hot
15 give me a ring
16 down in the mouth
17 stand in your way
18 A vicious circle

TEST 15

1 She was so beautiful that I couldn't take my eyes off her.
2 Winning that prize has gone to his head.
3 When he was a child he loved taking things to pieces – to see how they worked.
4 I do wish you'd stop biting your nails, Brian! It really gets on my nerves.
5 English people in general don't like making a fuss in public.
6 Could you keep an eye on my handbag for me while I go to the toilet?
7 She's not really upset; she's only putting on an act.
8 We're moving to Bristol next week but we promise to keep in touch.
9 You put your foot in it when you asked him where his wife was. Didn't you realise she was dead?
10 I hate the winter – it really gets me down.
11 It was hard to keep a straight face when she started to sing.
12 Many husbands often take their wives for granted; and vice-versa.
13 I happen to know the manager of the firm you've applied to for a job. I can put in a good word for you, if you like.
14 "All this took place a long, long time ago," said the history teacher to the class.
15 Many people nowadays find it increasingly difficult to make (both) ends meet.

TEST 16

Across
3 mountain (You're exaggerating the importance of something; you're making a small difficulty or problem seem like a big one)
6 package (A group holiday arranged by a travel agency where the travel and accommodation are paid for beforehand)

7   keep   (So as not to forget how to teach)
8   crow   (If you travel in a straight line)
9   hand   (A big round of applause)
10 business   (Don't interfere in things that don't concern you)
14 tongue   (A "slip of the tongue" is a careless mistake you make when speaking)
15 collar   (He got angry, upset or embarrassed)
16 flies   (Time passes very quickly)
18 bite   (There's no need to lose your temper with me; to shout at me)

Down
1   soaked   (We were very wet)
2   figures   (He is very good at mathematics, especially arithmetic)
4   handy   (It might be useful in the future)
5   heels   (To fall madly in love)
10 blue   (The letter arrived unexpectedly)
11 silver   (He was born into a rich family)
12 stick   (You've misunderstood me completely)
13 inside   (Someone who worked at the bank had helped to plan and carry out the robbery)
16 fire   (They get on really well together)
17 swing   (It's very small)

TEST 17

1   e   (He was caught as he was committing the crime)
2   i   (She was dismissed from her job)
3   m   ("Many Happy Returns" is the most common way of congratulating someone on his/her birthday)
4   k   (She is very clumsy and will probably break the cups, plates, etc.)
5   n   (My visits are very infrequent)
6   a   (He was going bald)
7   l   (No one else was able to say a word because he talked so much)
8   f   (Used to describe someone who is in a bad mood)
9   d   (You'd better make a greater effort)
10 h   (Let's stop quarrelling with one another)
11 o   (He spoke in a husky voice because of a small amount of mucus lodged in his throat)
12 j   (We don't agree with one another)
13 c   (He spoke without notes or without preparing the speech beforehand)
14 g   (He was extremely timid)
15 b   (I got into trouble)

TEST 18

1   I wouldn't believe everything completely; I'd assume only part of what he says is true.
2   It has been a tremendous success in New York.
3   I found it difficult not to say something; to remain silent.
4   I told him I didn't want any money back, that he could have the 50p change as a tip.
5   It will stop her from worrying or being anxious.
6   You can see who makes the decisions; you can see which person in the relationship is the dominant one.
7   His car is so damaged that it cannot be repaired and used again.
8   An alcoholic drink taken before going to bed.
9   The book is not available as all copies of it have been sold and it is not being reprinted by the original publisher.
10 I only started liking them after trying them for some time. (It is something one must learn to like.)
11 I think we ought to stop working.
12 Listen very carefully to what I am saying.
13 I got it very cheaply.
14 How could you break your promise?
15 We're relying on you to be in charge of things/to look after things until we get back.

TEST 19

1   e   (A "short cut" is a shorter way than usual)
2   k   (It's my job to make you go away)
3   h   (Why don't you behave in an adult and mature manner?)
4   a   (He told me to relax; not to worry about problems)
5   g   (I'm just going to bed)
6   l   (I'd love to come to your flat/house for a chat)
7   c   (You were dismissed from the garage; you lost your job)

8 j (Is it noticeable?)
9 f (A "white lie" is an unimportant lie – often told so as not to hurt another person's feelings)
10 b (I picked up her wig accidentally)
11 d (He's very tame; not at all aggressive)
12 i (He's been very good; he's behaved extremely well)

TEST 20

1 **goose** (It really put an end to his plans, hopes)
2 **cat** (My mother told everyone the secret)
3 **horse** (You're wasting your time)
4 **donkey** (It's a very long time since I last saw her)
5 **dogs** (Harold no longer takes care of himself; his appearance etc. has deteriorated)
6 **goat** (What makes me angry; what annoys me)
7 **birds** (I decided to make use of one occasion to do two things)
8 **bull** (He decided to take the bold step immediately of asking her to marry him)
9 **cows** (She could watch it for long periods of time without getting bored)
10 **fish** (There are plenty of other people for you to meet and have a relationship with. Used to try to comfort someone who has just lost a boyfriend or girlfriend)
11 **pig** (He ate far too much)
12 **crocodile** (Her tears are not real)
13 **lion** (He and his sister got the largest share)
14 **rat** (The "rat race" is the constant struggle for success in business or in one's job, etc.)
15 **kittens** (They're going to be in a state of panic)
16 **stag** (A "stag party" is given when a man about to get married has a party for his male friends)

TEST 21

1 False (A "tight-fisted" person doesn't like spending money)
2 True
3 False (It is a compliment. It means someone thinks you are a kind-hearted, generous person)
4 False (It has something to do with a wedding. It is when you announce a forthcoming marriage publicly in church)
5 True (A "hen party" is given when a woman about to get married has a party for her female friends)
6 False (It is to listen deliberately to a private conversation. To "overhear" is to listen accidentally to a private conversation)
7 False (It means to bribe someone; to pay someone for favours)
8 True
9 True
10 False (It means to trick or deceive someone)
11 True
12 False (It means it was very successful)
13 False (It means to have very little chance of getting the job)
14 True (A "windfall" is an unexpected gift or sum of money)
15 False (A thick-skinned person is someone who is very insensitive to criticism; who is not easily offended)
16 True (He ignored it)

TEST 22

1 f grey matter
2 i a piece of cake
3 l shoplifting
4 o a tall story
5 a a blessing in disguise
6 p a white-collar worker
7 j a practical joke
8 b a blue-collar worker
9 n a storm in a teacup
10 g a nest-egg
11 c a dead-end job
12 k a red-letter day
13 h a pain in the neck
14 d elbow grease
15 m a shot in the dark
16 e a false alarm

TEST 23

1 b **off his head** (The person must be crazy)
2 c **clocked in** (To "clock in" is to place a card in a machine to register the time when you start and finish work)
3 a **fine** (You left yourself very little time)
4 d **a line** (She would write to them)
5 b **got cold feet** (I lost courage; I became afraid)

6   c   **sleep on it**   (I'd like to think about it for a while before I give you my decision)
7   d   **off the record**   (It is unofficial; it is not for publication)
8   a   **ratty**   (Irritable)
9   c   **hand in glove**   (The police are working very closely with the Football Association)
10 d   **cup of tea**   (They are not things that I like)
11 b   **golden handshake**   (A large payment given to someone leaving a company or organisation)
12 b   **death warmed up**   (He looked terrible)
13 d   **hang**   (She soon got used to using it)
14 b   **mind**   (He is worried about something)

TEST 24

1   **on the shelf**   (Unmarried, and with no prospects of getting married)
2   **on the house**   (Free)
3   **on principle**   (As a matter of principle because of her fixed beliefs in socialism)
4   **on the dot**   (At 9 o'clock exactly)
5   **on account of**   (Because of; due to)
6   **on the spur of the moment**   (Without planning beforehand; impulsively)
7   **on average**   (Most teachers earn about £1,000 a month)
8   **on the rocks**   (The company will soon be bankrupt)
9   **on the whole**   (Overall, generally)
10 **on and off**   (Irregularly; from time to time)
11 **on your toes**   (Alert; ready to act)
12 **on the carpet**   (Told off; reprimanded by one's boss)
13 **on the other hand**   ("On the one hand ... on the other". Used to emphasise the contrast between two opposite statements)
14 **on board**   (As soon as I step onto the boat)
15 **on the run**   (Fleeing from the police)
16 **on call**   (Available for duty)
17 **on tenterhooks**   (Very nervous; be in a state of nervous suspense)
18 **on the contrary**   (Used to contradict what has been said. The truth is the opposite of what has been said)
19 **on the cards**   (Possible; likely)
20 **on purpose**   (You did it deliberately)

TEST 25

1   c   **a bell**   (He had a very clear voice)
2   b   **a daisy**   (He woke up feeling very refreshed)
3   a   **nails**   (He's very hard and ruthless; he doesn't have much feeling for other people)
4   b   **lead**   (It's very heavy)
5   d   **large**   (Used to show that you saw someone you didn't expect to see)
6   a   **a mule**   (He's very stubborn)
7   c   **a judge**   (I'm completely sober)
8   b   **a rock**   (It's very steady)
9   a   **thieves**   (They were very friendly with each other and spent a great deal of their time together)
10 d   **a beetroot**   (I always blush)
11 b   **houses**   (It's completely safe)
12 c   **a log**   (She slept soundly)
13 d   **a horse**   (He eats a lot)
14 a   **a chimney**   (She smoked a lot)
15 b   **a glove**   (It fits perfectly)
16 c   **a sieve**   (He's got a very bad memory)
17 b   **ton**   (He'll be very angry)
18 c   **a house on fire**   (They got on really well together; they became great friends)
19 a   **wildfire**   (The news spread very quickly)
20 b   **a leaf**   (She was trembling)

TEST 26

Vanity/Conceit
bigheaded   (Vain, conceited)
stuck-up   (Proud, conceited)
too big for one's boots   (Having too high an opinion of oneself)

Unhappiness
browned off   (Fed up; depressed)
down-hearted   (Depressed; very sad)
down in the dumps   (Unhappy; depressed)

Money
feather one's nest   (Make oneself rich in a job – usually in a dishonest or illegal way)
keep one's head above water   (Keep out of debt; avoid money problems)
on a shoestring   (On a very small budget)

Fear
hair-raising   (Frightening; causing a state of fear or panic)
have one's heart in one's mouth   (Be very afraid)
put the wind up someone   (Frighten someone)

Anxiety/Worry
have something on one's mind   (Be worried about something)
keyed up   (Be tense or nervous)
on tenterhooks   (Be nervous; be in a state of nervous suspense)

Ill-health
feel under the weather   (Feel slightly ill)
off colour   (Look slightly unwell)
out of sorts   (Be slightly ill)

Alcohol
Dutch courage   (Courage obtained by drinking alcohol)
see pink elephants   (To be drunk; to have far too much to drink)
tipsy   (Slightly drunk)

Anger
fly off the handle   (Lose one's temper; become angry)
go off the deep end   (Lose one's temper; become angry)
see red   (Lose one's temper; become angry)

Disagreement/Argument
at loggerheads   (Always quarrelling)
have a bone to pick with someone   (To complain to someone about something; have a reason to quarrel with someone)
have words   (Have an argument)

Age
getting on in years   (Growing old)
long in the tooth   (Be old)
past one's prime   (Past one's best years; starting to grow old)

TEST 27

Across
 3 name   (He is becoming famous)
 4 water   (They are not logical or reliable when tested)
 5 stone   (It's very difficult; it's almost impossible)
 7 foggiest   (I have no idea)
11 break   (To show neither profit nor loss)
12 dogs   (To "let sleeping dogs lie" is to avoid mentioning a subject which could cause trouble)
15 donkey   (All the hard, real work)
16 head   (Go to a higher authority than the person you are talking to)
17 short   (I don't have much money this month)
19 minds   (I'm undecided)

Down
 1 stiff   (For not showing their feelings – especially when in trouble)
 2 point   (Reach the most important thing you want to say; reach the main point in a discussion)
 3 never   (It is better to arrive late than not to arrive at all)
 6 chip   (Have a grudge about something; feel bitter about something)
 8 once   (For the last time)
 9 shoulder   (She ignored me completely)
10 looks   (He got some angry and disapproving looks from the other passengers)
13 sheep   (The disreputable member of the family; a family member who has done something to make the other members of the family feel ashamed of him/her)
14 passed   (Died)
18 thick   (Insensitive to criticism; who is not easily offended)

TEST 28

 1 **hands**   (He found himself with lots of free time)
 2 **stomach**   (You need to be able to see blood, dead bodies, etc. without feeling sick)
 3 **cheek** (nerve)   (He then dared to complain about his breakfast being cold)
 4 **tooth**   (If you have a sweet tooth, you like eating sweet things)
 5 **back**   (They were glad to see him leave)
 6 **legs**   (I'll go for a walk)

7   **brains**   (Do you mind if I talk to you in order to get information to use for my essay?)
8   **nerve**   (He became frightened and could no longer climb mountains)
9   **arms**   (The viewers were very angry)
10   **finger**   (I can't say exactly what is wrong)
11   **blood**   (It makes me very angry)
12   **hair**   (Keep calm! Don't panic!)
13   **chest**   (When you get a problem off your chest, you tell someone else about it)
14   **breast**   (She decided to confess)
15   **heart**   (She takes every criticism personally)
16   **bones**   (I can feel it strongly; I am quite sure there is going to be trouble although I cannot explain why)
17   **foot**   (Our relationship has started badly)
18   **mouth**   (To "put words into someone's mouth" is to pretend that someone has said something that he or she has not actually said)

TEST 29

1   f   (It is better to be honest than to try to deceive people. By being honest you gain the lasting trust of others)
2   h   (It is better to do something after a delay rather than not do it at all; it is better to arrive late rather than not arrive at all)
3   k   (Someone who is quiet and says very little often hides deep feelings or a lot of knowledge on a subject)
4   p   (We judge a person by what he or she does rather than by what that person says he or she will do)
5   a   (When you try to do something in a hurry, there is a tendency to make careless mistakes and, consequently, to take even longer to do the particular task than if you had not tried to hurry in the first place)
6   j   (A foolish person spends his or her money without thought and is soon penniless. It is also very easy to persuade a foolish person to spend his or her money on worthless and unnecessary things)
7   l   (When something difficult ends happily or satisfactorily, there is no need to complain or be disappointed about the trouble it may have caused)
8   b   (Someone who is constantly changing his or her job or moving from place to place will never become rich or successful)
9   o   (By acting quickly at an early stage, you may be able to prevent serious trouble in the future)
10   n   (Never be too optimistic about something; don't believe or expect that victory or success is certain until it actually happens)
11   m   (Choose the right moment to act – the time when you are most likely to succeed; take advantage of a sudden opportunity)
12   d   (Don't do anything or say anything that will stir up unnecessary trouble; don't look for trouble on purpose)
13   i   (Never act hastily. Consider carefully what you are going to do before you do it)
14   c   (If you have been cheated or deceived on one occasion by someone or something, you will be very careful when you meet that person or thing again)
15   e   (Always try to take advantage of favourable circumstances. Also, have a good time while one can)
16   g   (A job cannot be done properly if it is done too quickly. This phrase is also often used as an excuse for delay)

TEST 30

1   g   do time
2   k   have a good time
3   a   be an old hand at something
4   h   get one's own back
5   o   make a scene
6   i   give someone a black look
7   b   be out of pocket
8   n   keep on one's toes
9   e   come to a head
10   m   hold one's horses
11   c   break one's word
12   f   come to light
13   p   put one's feet up
14   d   bring something to mind
15   l   have one's hands full
16   j   give someone the slip

TEST 31

1   c   **do**   ("Do nicely" means that it would be very suitable)
2   d   **down at heel**   (He looked very dirty and poor)
3   a   **fist**   (He's been making a lot of money very quickly and easily)
4   b   **practice**   (We haven't played enough tennis)
5   d   **tea in China**   (Nothing would induce me to move there)
6   b   **burning the candle at both ends**   (He's been going to bed late and getting up early)

7   b   **tip**   (I could almost remember her name, but not quite)
8   c   **inside out**   (The inside of the jumper was on the outside)
9   d   **hit the nail on the head**   (You've said exactly the right thing)
10   b   **fingers**   (I hope you will be lucky)
11   a   **spilt**   (It's no use being sorry about something that has happened and that cannot be changed)
12   b   **in print**   (He always wanted to write and get his work published)
13   d   **a hair's breadth**   (He or she only narrowly missed hitting the pedestrian)
14   c   **sore**   (A "sight for sore eyes" is something or someone that you are pleased to see)
15   a   **chin**   (Don't be discouraged; be brave)

TEST 32

1   k   (How much do we owe the bank?)
2   h   (I'm going to have a really good time, e.g. by going to bars, nightclubs, etc.)
3   j   (It isn't working properly)
4   l   (The minimum number of staff that can run an office or a factory)
5   a   (I've been falsifying the firm's accounts; I've been embezzling the firm's money)
6   i   (Who's in a bad mood this morning?)
7   c   (You're dismissed; you've lost your job)
8   f   (I'm terrified, very frightened of the thought of retirement)
9   d   (I think someone wants us to hurry up)
10   g   (Lots of men are going bald)
11   e   (Don't tell anyone else about this)
12   b   (Of course she's nervous)

TEST 33

1   **for a change**   (As a change from what we usually do)
2   **off the beaten track**   (Out-of-the-way; away from towns, villages; in a lonely place)
3   **out of breath**   (Unable to breathe easily because of running, working hard, etc.)
4   **by no means**   (It is not at all unusual)
5   **out of hand**   (The demonstration got out of control)
6   **for the time being**   (For the moment; temporarily)
7   **by hand**   (People make them individually, rather than being mass-produced by machines)
8   **off duty**   (When she stopped work)
9   **By the way**   (Incidentally. Used to introduce a subject)
10   **out of tune**   (The notes don't sound right; the pitch is incorrect)
11   **off the top of his head**   (Without preparing beforehand; spontaneously)
12   **by far**   (Compared to all the others; by a large margin)
13   **out of bounds**   (They were forbidden to go inside the fish and chip shop)
14   **off and on**   (From time to time; periodically)
15   **for good**   (I shall leave this country and never come back again)
16   **out of the question**   (It's quite impossible)
17   **by chance**   (Unintentionally; unexpectedly)
18   **for short**   (Ben is a short form of Benjamin)
19   **for the high jump**   (Mr Wilson's going to be punished)
20   **by heart**   (To memorise them)

TEST 34

1   f   (You tend to feel more affection for someone when you have been away from him or her for a while)
2   j   (You cannot really judge a person by looks alone. Physical beauty may hide a very ugly nature, for instance)
3   m   (Those who arrive first will be served or dealt with first; those who arrive early get a better choice)
4   k   (When the person in authority is away, e.g. the boss, those under him can do as they like – especially misbehave in some way)
5   o   (If we receive no news about someone or something we are interested in, then we can assume that nothing bad has happened)
6   c   (Whether you miss your objective by a narrow margin or a wide margin, you have still failed)
7   l   (If someone has done something kind or helpful to you, you should express your gratitude by doing something kind or helpful to him or her in return)
8   a   (It is better to be content with something you are already sure of getting than to lose it by trying to get something better later on)
9   g   (A bad workman will often blame his tools for a bad job rather than his own lack of skill in using them)

10 b (You should help your own family or people in your own country before you help others)
11 n (The more often you do something the better you become at it; only by doing something again and again can you become really proficient)
12 e (When you are faced with a very difficult problem you will use all your skill and energy in trying to solve or overcome it; when we need something so much that we cannot do without it, we are forced into finding a way of getting it)
13 h (A new boss is likely to make changes to try to improve the efficiency of the company he or she is now in charge of)
14 p (The things that one person likes are not necessarily those liked by someone else; different people like different things)
15 d (If too many people try to do a job or activity at the same time, it will probably go wrong or be spoilt or damaged)
16 i (When a person is really determined to do something, then no matter how difficult it may be, he or she will try to find a way of doing it)

TEST 35

1 False ("Once in a blue moon" means very rarely)
2 True
3 True
4 False (It should be "second-hand")
5 True
6 True
7 False (An "old maid" is a woman who has never got married)
8 False (If he is "pushing up daisies", he's dead)
9 True
10 False (You would not usually feel proud if you were dismissed from your job)
11 False (He might eat like a horse, perhaps. To "eat your heart out" means to be very sad or distressed about something; to worry excessively)
12 True (They are two of the extra advantages you get on top of your regular salary)
13 True (We ate baked potatoes)
14 False (If you are "in the doghouse" you are being treated in an unfriendly way, usually because you have offended that person in some way. It is often used with couples, the husband or wife being in the doghouse for one reason or another)
15 True (The book is damaged; the corners of the pages are bent down with use)
16 False (A "weedy" person is someone who is very thin and weak-looking)

TEST 36

1 Give me a ring if you feel like going out for a meal one day next week.
2 That wasn't what I meant at all! You've got hold of the wrong end of the stick as usual!
3 We can take our time; the play doesn't start until 7.30.
4 The fact that the President had been a drug addict didn't come to light until several years after his death.
5 I may not come first in the race, but I'll do my best not to come last.
6 My husband has football on the brain; it's the only thing he thinks about.
7 We're organising a going-away party for Sue on Saturday. But keep it quiet as it's supposed to be a surprise.
8 If things go wrong, James, whatever you do, don't lose your head.
9 More than 1,000 runners took part in this year's Manchester marathon.
10 The way he took everything she did for granted really put her back up.
11 The personnel officer gave (him) her word that she wouldn't tell anyone that he had been in prison.
12 We'd get the job finished much quicker if everyone pulled his/her weight.
13 If you don't like the idea then just say so. I believe you should call a spade a spade.
14 My father's going to go up the wall when he finds out that I've lost the car keys.
15 Don't take any notice of what he says; he's only trying to annoy you.

TEST 37

Across

1	fuss	16	disappointed
6	criticising	18	relax
7	decide	22	deliberately
8	mean	23	infrequent
9	exhausted	25	irrelevant
12	moment	26	frightened
13	commotion		

Down

2	unemployed	15	wasted
3	freed	17	useless
4	inexperienced	19	pay
5	honest	20	progress
10	intelligent	21	disagree
11	hurry	24	crazy
14	complete		

TEST 38

1 **sharp** (Using words that are intended to hurt the person you are speaking to)
2 **foregone** (The result could be predicted in advance)
3 **unwritten** (A code of behaviour which everyone knows about and obeys)
4 **weak** (She wasn't very good at spelling)
5 **naked** (Without binoculars or a telescope)
6 **dark** (A person whose true abilities are unknown but may be better than is generally thought)
7 **practical** (A trick played upon someone, often to make the person look silly)
8 **sore** (A subject which upsets or annoys him)
9 **fair** (She will deal with you fairly and honestly)
10 **confirmed** (He has decided never to get married)
11 **tall** (A story that is so incredible that it is difficult to believe it is true)
12 **hot** (A direct telephone link)
13 **wishful** (Wanting something to be true that can never be)
14 **bated** (They held their breath as they waited, nervously, for the results)
15 **broad** (When it was light)
16 **rough** (Approximately 300)
17 **pet** (One of the things he hated most)
18 **flat** (My car had a puncture)
19 **golden** (An excellent opportunity)
20 **square** (The first proper meal)

TEST 39

a   6   (who has been caught doing something wrong – often illegal)
b   11 (who has been narrowly beaten in a race)
c   16 (who has just gone to bed)
d   13 (who has said when he/she is getting married)
e   7   (who is working when others are on strike)
f   1   (who is old-fashioned)
g   10 (who is really enjoying himself/herself)
h   9   (who is in the public eye)
i   4   (who is doing exercises)
j   5   (who is a thief)
k   14 (who is working)
l   2   (who is not very fit)
m   15 (who is putting up with hardships; who is doing without modern conveniences)
n   3   (who is extremely busy)
o   12 (who is doing something to impress others and to show how good he/she is)
p   8   (who is running away)

TEST 40

1 **shoulders** (Much better than the others)
2 **sweet** (Very short and to the point)
3 **large** (On the whole; generally speaking)
4 **thumbs** (He's very clumsy)
5 **soul** (She was the person who made the party lively)
6 **square** (Fairly)
7 **about** (Recovered and out of bed)
8 **void** (Invalid; not legally binding)
9 **bull** (A story that isn't true)
10 **sound** (Safe and unharmed)
11 **thin** (They promised to stand by each other whatever happened)
12 **tear** (It gets a lot of use; people walk on it a lot)
13 **blood** (Family member; relative)
14 **take** (Compromise)
15 **span** (Clean and tidy)
16 **fast** (Very strict)
17 **nail** (Fight or argue fiercely)
18 **front** (The front of the jumper was at the back and the back of the jumper was at the front)
19 **cons** (Advantages and disadvantages)
20 **tired** (Really fed up with hearing about his children; I don't want to hear about his children any more)

TEST 41

1	f	egg someone on	9	d	call someone's bluff
2	o	pull one's socks up	10	l	lose face
3	k	live from hand to mouth	11	a	bark up the wrong tree
4	g	hear something on the grapevine	12	p	rub someone up the wrong way
5	n	pick holes in something	13	h	jump down someone's throat
6	i	jump out of the frying pan and into the fire	14	b	bide one's time
			15	j	lend someone a hand
7	c	butter someone up	16	e	cut someone dead
8	m	lose one's temper			

TEST 42

1 **on** (My house is burning)
2 **under** (She makes all the decisions; she is the dominant partner in the marriage)
3 **at** (Ten hours without stopping)
4 **to; behind** (Tell me directly. I hate people who do things secretly)
5 **on** (She never does it, because she doesn't believe in tipping)
6 **Between** (What I am saying is in strict confidence)
7 **At** (If we continue at the same speed it'll be Christmas before it's finished)
8 **for** (Nothing would make me part with it)
9 **in** (The party was already very lively when they got there)
10 **off** (He had to give a speech completely unprepared; he had to give an impromptu speech)
11 **on** (He was tense, nervous)
12 **in** (I wouldn't like to be her)
13 **up to** (I have far too much work to do)
14 **away** (Yvonne revealed the secret)
15 **off** (Getting rid of his aggressions)
16 **in** (He felt like crying)
17 **out of** (It's really tasty)
18 **off** (Don't talk nonsense! That's rubbish!)

TEST 43

1 **black** (The illegal market)
2 **blue** (It doesn't matter what you say to her, she won't listen to you)
3 **green** (They were given permission to go ahead with the new project)
4 **black** (Not very popular with her at the moment)
5 **blue** (The news came very suddenly and unexpectedly)
6 **white** (Useless, expensive presents)
7 **grey** (Lacking in intelligence)
8 **red** (A very important day for my sister and her husband)
9 **brown** (She was very sun-tanned)
10 **red** (An attempt to draw attention away from this month's poor sales figures)
11 **white** (She went very pale)
12 **yellow** (I'm too much of a coward)
13 **black; white** (In writing)
14 **blue** (He's been the boss's favourite)
15 **red** (It makes him very angry)
16 **green** (I was very envious)
17 **pink** (He was really pleased)
18 **blue** (Pornographic films)
19 **white** (An unimportant lie, usually so as not to hurt someone's feelings)
20 **red** (She always blushes when she gets embarrassed)

TEST 44

1	ON THE CARDS	8	WHOLE-HEARTED	15	IN THE BALANCE
2	TURN OVER A NEW LEAF	9	IN HIS/HER BIRTHDAY SUIT	16	SHELVES
				17	TOE THE LINE
3	UP TO SCRATCH	10	SPILL THE BEANS	18	FROM SCRATCH
4	IN DEEP WATER	11	EAT HIS/HER WORDS	19	UNDER WAY
5	POPS THE QUESTION	12	IN THE BAG	20	HUSH MONEY
6	LAY OFF	13	WHITE PAPER		
7	BROKEN-HEARTED	14	AT LARGE		

TEST 45

1 f (A "bottleneck" is where the road narrows so that a traffic-jam is quickly formed)
2 i (This is the imaginary line made by workers on strike, trying to persuade others to join them)
3 l (When you have a lot of weapons)
4 n (When you are in prison)
5 b (To ease the tension, nervousness, shyness when you first meet people)
6 r (Is very effective)
7 q (Courage obtained by drinking alcohol)
8 a (A husband who is constantly nagged by his wife)
9 p (To be very frightened)
10 g (Very quickly)
11 o (A speech that is long and boring; a speaker talking at great length about something)
12 c (Be careful about the way one behaves; be on one's best behaviour)
13 k (Available for duty)
14 e (Honest, sincere)
15 h (The notes – e.g. of a musical instrument – don't sound right)
16 d (Try to deceive someone)
17 j (To insist)
18 m (Speak to an audience; get up to speak in a debate)

TEST 46

1 b **shell** (He'll stop being shy)
2 c **horse's mouth** (I got it directly from someone who knows)
3 a **boots** (He has too high an opinion of himself)
4 d **hop** (You've arrived when I wasn't expecting you; you've caught me unexpectedly)
5 b **a duck's back** (No matter what you say, it has absolutely no effect on her)
6 c **jackets** (Potatoes with the peel still on. They are usually baked in the oven)
7 c **spitting** (She looks exactly like Marilyn Monroe)
8 a **budding** (One of the few composers who is developing well)
9 c **rope** (It's a very easy way to make money)
10 d **wives'** (A foolish and false belief, often to do with medicine, which at one time people believed to be true)
11 a **hangover** (The feeling of headache and general sickness you feel the day after you have drunk too much alcohol)
12 b **long** (A "long shot" is something which has very little chance of success)
13 a **nook** (We looked everywhere)
14 d **ointment** (A minor disadvantage which stops you enjoying something fully)
15 b **crying** (It's a great shame)
16 d **blanket** (She takes the pleasure out of everything by being very negative and constantly finding fault with things)
17 c **catcalls** (Sharp cries and whistles of disapproval)
18 a **final fling** (He wanted to enjoy himself for one last time before getting married)
19 d **spot** (He was very fond of his niece)
20 b **general dogsbody** (A "general dogsbody" is someone who is like a slave because everyone gives him/her orders)